# All Sorts of Things

**THEODORE CLYMER · GRETCHEN WULFING**

CONSULTANTS

ROGER W. SHUY · E. PAUL TORRANCE
LINGUISTICS             CREATIVITY

**GINN AND COMPANY**
A XEROX COMPANY

# Acknowledgments

Grateful acknowledgement is made to the following authors and publishers for permission to use copyrighted materials:

The Bobbs-Merrill Company, Inc., for "How Beaver Got His Fine Fur" from *The Long-Tailed Bear and Other Indian Legends,* copyright © 1961, by Natalia M. Belting, reprinted by permission of the publishers, the Bobbs-Merrill Company, Inc.

Brandt & Brandt for "Jimmy Takes Vanishing Lessons," adapted from *Jimmy Takes Vanishing Lessons,* by Walter R. Brooks. Copyright 1950 by Walter R. Brooks. Reprinted by permission of Alfred A. Knopf, Inc.

Coward-McCann, Inc., for "The Flute Player of Beppu," adapted by permission of Coward-McCann, Inc., from *The Flute Player of Beppu* by Kathryn Gallant, © 1960 Kathryn Gallant and Kurt Weiss.

J. M. Dent & Sons Ltd., London, for the first verse of "Adventures of Isabel" from *Many Long Years Ago* by Ogden Nash. By permission of J. M. Dent & Sons Ltd.

Doubleday & Company, Inc., for "Tides" from *Taxis and Toadstools* by Rachel Field. Copyright 1926 by Doubleday & Company, Inc. Reprinted by permission of the publisher.

E. P. Dutton & Co., Inc., for "The Night Workers" from *The Night Workers* by Alvin Schwartz. Copyright, ©, 1966 by Alvin Schwartz. Condensed and reprinted by permission of E. P. Dutton & Co., Inc. Also for first stanza of "America the Beautiful" from *Poems* by Katharine Lee Bates. Reprinted by permission of E. P. Dutton & Co., Inc.

Harcourt Brace Jovanovich, Inc., for Haiku by Soeseki and Chosu from *Cricket Songs: Japanese Haiku,* translated and © 1964 by Harry Behn. Reprinted by permission of Harcourt Brace Jovanovich, Inc.

Harper & Row, Publishers, for "Flat Stanley," an approved adaptation of *Flat Stanley* by Jeff Brown with selected illustrations by Tomi Ungerer. Text copyright © 1964 by Jeff Brown. Pictures copyright © 1964 by Tomi Ungerer.

Holt, Rinehart and Winston, Inc., for "The Wonderful Visit to Miss Liberty," condensed and adapted from *The Wonderful Visit to Miss Liberty* by Elizabeth Starr Hill. Copyright © 1961 by Elizabeth Starr Hill. Reprinted by permission of Holt, Rinehart and Winston, Inc.

J. B. Lippincott Company for "Snowstorm Before Christmas," adapted from *Snow Storm Before Christmas* by Candida Palmer. Copyright © 1965 by Candida Palmer. Published by J. B. Lippincott Company. Also for "I Wouldn't" and "All About Boys and Girls" from *You Read to Me, I'll Read to You* by John Ciardi. Copyright © 1962 by John Ciardi. Published by J. B. Lippincott Company.

Little, Brown and Company for "Money of Long Ago," adapted from *Nails to Nickels: The Story of American Coins Old and New* by Elizabeth A. Campbell. Copyright ©, 1960, by Elizabeth Anderson Campbell and Leonard Weisgard. By permission of Little, Brown and Company. And first verse of "Adventures of Isabel" from *Many Long Years Ago* by Ogden Nash. Copyright 1936, by Ogden Nash. By permission of Little, Brown and Company.

The Macmillan Company for "City Lights" from *Poems* by Rachel Field, copyright, 1924, 1930, by the Macmillan Company; for "Snow in the City" from *Branches Green* by Rachel Field, copyright, 1934, by The Macmillan Company; and for "The Hairy Dog" from *Pillicock Hill* by Herbert Asquith. All used by permission of The Macmillan Company.

W. W. Norton & Company, Inc., for "The Dragon in the Clock Box," reprinted from *The Dragon in the Clock Box* by M. Jean Craig. Illustrated by Kelly Oechsli. Text copyright © 1962 by M. Jean Craig. Illustrations Copyright © 1962 by Kelly Oechsli.

Random House, Inc., for "Jimmy Takes Vanishing Lessons," adapted from *Jimmy Takes Vanishing Lessons,* by Walter R. Brooks. Copyright 1950 by Walter R. Brooks. Reprinted by permission of Alfred A. Knopf; Inc. Also for the playlet "Snow-White and Rose-Red," © Copyright 1969 by Gretchen Wulfing and Random House, Inc. Adapted to play form from the Hunt/Stern translation of the Grimm story, "Snow White and Rose Red," by permission of Pantheon Books, Inc., A Division of Random House, Inc.

The Evelyn Singer Agency for "Man-Made Giants" from *Machines at Work* by Mary Elting. Library of Congress Catalog Card No. 62-17249. Copyright 1953, 1962 by Duenwald Printing Corp. By permission of the Evelyn Singer Agency and Harvey House, Inc.

The Viking Press, Inc., for "The Desert People," adapted from *The Desert People* by Ann Nolan Clark. Copyright © 1962 by Ann Nolan Clark. All rights reserved. Reprinted by permission of The Viking Press, Inc.

The World Publishing Company for "The World's Smartest Cat," from *Idy, the Fox-Chasing Cow and Other Stories* by Ellen Margolis. Adapted by arrangement with The World Publishing Company. Copyright © 1962 by Ellen Margolis. All rights reserved.

Abelard-Schuman Limited for "Great Day in Ghana," adapted from *Great Day in Ghana: Kwasi Goes to Town* by Geraldine Kaye. Copyright © 1962, by Abelard-Schuman Limited. By permission of Abelard-Schuman Limited. All Rights Reserved. Also for "The Skating Race," adapted from *Great Day in Holland: The Skating Race* by Rutgers van der Loeff. Copyright © 1965, by Abelard-Schuman Limited. By permission of Abelard-Schuman Limited. All Rights Reserved.

A. S. Barnes & Company, Inc., for "Kapoi and the Owl King," adapted from *Hawaiian Wonder Tales* by Post Wheeler. Copyright 1953. All Rights Reserved. Used by permission of the publisher.

Laura Benét for "Barnum's First Circus," adapted from her book *Barnum's First Circus and Other Stories,* copyright, 1949. Published by Dodd, Mead and Company.

*Child Life* for the poem "Our History" by Catherine Cate Coblentz, from *Child Life,* Copyright 1945.

Curtis Brown, Ltd., New York, for Haiku by Soseki and Chosu from *Cricket Songs* translated by Harry Behn, reprinted by permission of Curtis Brown, Ltd.,

## Illustrators

Donn Albright
Frans Altschuler
Ray Ameijide
Willi Baum
Mike Cassaro
Bernard D'Andrea
Ed Emberley

Lorraine Fox
Judy Sue Goodwin
George Guzzi
David Kelley
Gordon Laite
Dora Leder
Marie Michal

Jane Teiko Oka
Joan Paley
Jerry Pinkney
Albert John Pucci
Tomi Ungerer
Dianne Winer
Hans Zander

# Contents

## 3. Could It Be Magic?

## 4. The Workaday World

## 5. Before You Were Born

## 6. Magic of Old

BOOK-LENGTH STORY

# Jimmy Takes Vanishing Lessons,

# From Sea to Shining Sea

# America the Beautiful

O beautiful for spacious skies,
For amber waves of grain,
For purple mountain majesties
Above the fruited plain!
America! America!
God shed His grace on thee
And crown thy good with brotherhood
From sea to shining sea!

*Katharine Lee Bates*

8

# The Wonderful Visit to Miss Liberty

"This is a special day," Daddy said. "Today we're going to visit the Statue of Liberty."

"Is it in a building?" William asked.

His sister Bonnie laughed. "No," she said. "It's outdoors, on an island in New York harbor. My friend Ellen took a helicopter ride over New York. She told me the statue is as tall as her apartment house."

"I never knew a statue could be *that* big," William said.

Mother tied on her straw sun hat. "Almost ready?" she asked.

"All set," said Daddy. "Let's go!"

They piled into their car. As they drove off Bonnie asked, "Why is the statue called *Liberty?*"

"*Liberty* means *freedom,*" Daddy said. "One hundred years after we became a free country, the people of France gave us the Statue of Liberty."

"Like a sort of birthday present?" William asked.

"That's right," Daddy agreed. "Men in France made the big statue out of thin sheets of copper."

"It came to America on a ship," Mother said. "But it was too large to send in one piece, so it was sent over in many pieces. Then workmen put the pieces of copper together over an iron framework right on the island."

Daddy parked the car near the ferry that would take them to Liberty Island. Bonnie and William hopped out.

"There she is!" Bonnie cried. "There's the Statue of Liberty! She *is* as tall as an apartment house!"

Across the water, the Lady stood outlined against the sky, a torch held high in her right hand. William jumped up and down. "She has a crown on her head! Why is she green?"

"Copper turns green when it's out in the weather," Daddy told him. "See the stone pedestal she stands on? That was paid for by the American people. Even school children gave their money to help build it."

It was time to buy tickets for the ferry. They joined the line at the ticket window. The ferry was just docking. It was a small, high boat, with three decks.

"I want to go up there," William said, pointing. He led the way on board and up the stairs to the open deck.

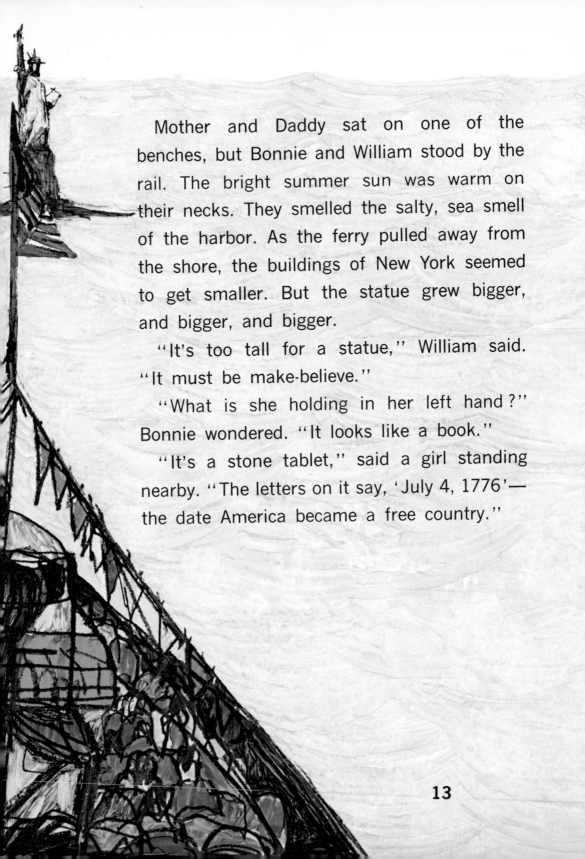

Mother and Daddy sat on one of the benches, but Bonnie and William stood by the rail. The bright summer sun was warm on their necks. They smelled the salty, sea smell of the harbor. As the ferry pulled away from the shore, the buildings of New York seemed to get smaller. But the statue grew bigger, and bigger, and bigger.

"It's too tall for a statue," William said. "It must be make-believe."

"What is she holding in her left hand?" Bonnie wondered. "It looks like a book."

"It's a stone tablet," said a girl standing nearby. "The letters on it say, 'July 4, 1776'— the date America became a free country."

"Ships come through here from nearly every country in the world," Daddy said. "The people on board stand by the ship's rail, just as you are now. When they see the Statue of Liberty, they know they've reached America."

Mother said, "As long as the Statue of Liberty stands here in the harbor, it will remind people everywhere that this is the land of freedom."

14

The ferry pulled alongside the dock with a bump. Mother and Daddy and Bonnie and William all hurried ashore. Now they were behind the statue. It towered above the small island.

"The whole island is no bigger than two or three blocks at home!" Bonnie cried.

They walked through thick, wooden doors in the wall beneath the pedestal. It seemed dim after the bright sunlight outdoors.

At the end of the hallway, an elevator operator called out, "Elevator to the top of the pedestal. Ten stories—going up!"

"You mean it's ten stories before we even get near the *feet* of the statue?" Bonnie gasped.

"That's right," the operator said. "Then another twelve stories after that, up to the observation room in her head."

William was startled. "Is the statue's head big enough for us to fit inside?"

"Sure is, sonny. Holds forty people. Fine sights from up there, through the windows in her crown."

As the elevator carried them up, the operator pressed a button. A voice told them that the only way to reach the observation room was by climbing a spiral staircase of one hundred and sixty-eight steps.

The staircase wound up and up. Every few steps there was a little built-in seat. The steps were tiny. Each one was as narrow as the seat of a swing.

"I've never been on such little stairs," Mother said.

Bonnie was just behind her. "These are William-size steps," she laughed.

Up and up, higher and higher they climbed. Bonnie's legs began to hurt. "I'm going to try the little seats," she said.

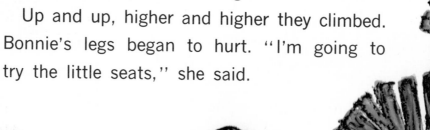

She sat in one of them. William sat in another. After they had rested for a minute, they climbed again.

Suddenly, they smelled fresh air. One by one, they stepped into the small, round observation room.

"Please hold me up," William begged his father. "I want to see out the front."

Mother and Daddy lifted both of them. The children gasped. How high they were! It was like being on a cloud. The whole harbor was stretched out below them. The New York skyscrapers were like paper cutouts pasted against the sky.

"I can look down on the tops of boats,"
Bonnie cried.

"I see one with freight trains on its back,"
William shouted. "I see a bridge. I can see
*everything* !"

19

The room became crowded, so Bonnie and William finally gave someone else a turn. They counted twenty-five windows. There were people in front of every one.

It was time to go. They climbed down, down, down the winding staircase.

As they boarded the elevator, the operator smiled at them. "Like it up there?"

William said, "We sure did!"

"We felt like the tallest people in the world," Bonnie told him.

On the ground floor, Mother and Daddy led the way from the elevator through a long hall. They stopped in front of a tablet on the wall.

Daddy read the last part of the tablet out loud: "I lift my lamp beside the golden door."

The children thought of all they had learned that day about their country, and about the meaning of the great statue.

William said slowly, "New York harbor is like a doorway to America."

Bonnie remembered what Mother had said before. "As long as the Statue of Liberty stands here in the harbor," she said, "it will remind people everywhere that this is the land of freedom."

*Elizabeth Starr Hill*

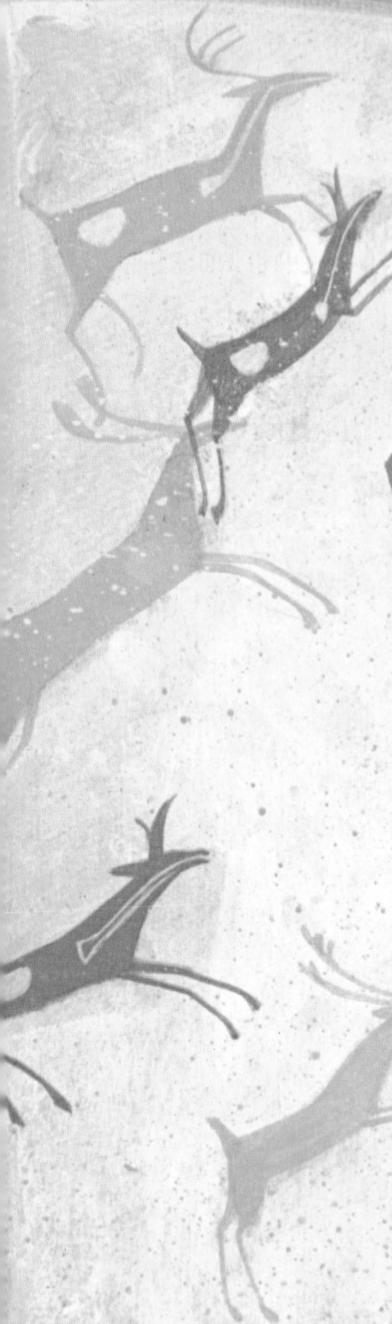

# A Song of Greatness

When I hear the old men
Telling of heroes,
Telling of great deeds
Of ancient days,
When I hear that telling
Then I think within me
I too, am one of these.

When I hear the people
Praising great ones,
Then I know that I too
Shall be esteemed,
I too when my time comes
Shall do mightily.

*Mary Austin*

22

# THE DESERT PEOPLE

I am a boy
  of the Desert People.

White men call me Indian.
White men call me Papago
  but the wild animals
  call me Brother
  because they know me
  and love me.

We call ourselves
  the Desert People.

I live in a village
  in the desert country,
  the flat sand country,
  the hot dry country.

23

Purple mountains fence it.
Hot winds sweep it.
Heat mist fills it
   and above us
   hangs the empty
   turquoise sky.

My village is here
   in the desert.

The name of my village is
   Place-Where-Waters-Meet.

In the Rainy Moon,
   when the rains pour down,
   rain waters run
   to the dry-wash there,
   overflowing its banks
   to give our thirsty fields
   rain water to drink.

It is good to live
   at Place-Where-Waters-Meet.

My village has houses
of ocotillo and cactus ribs
It has no streets.

Each house has a yard
fenced with cactus ribs
and swept
clean and bare.

Each house has a ramada
made of mesquite posts
and roofed with branches.

In the ramada
are the bedrolls
of the family
for night sleeping.

Hanging from the roof poles
is the water olla
damp and cool.

The houses of my village
   belong to my father
   and to my uncles
   and to my uncles' sons.

We live here together,
   the men and the boys,
   the women and the girls,
   in peace and happiness,
   with laughter and song.

My village has a Rain House,
   round-shaped,
   branch-covered,
   a holy place.

To the Rain House
   each night
   the men may go
   to make Song Magic.

Women and children
  sit outside.
They may hear the songs.
They may not sing them.

It is good
  to be a boy
  of the Desert People.
I am happy
  and proud.

We have ways
  of doing things
  that have been given
  to us
  by Desert People
  who have gone
  before us.

These ways are our ways.
We must not forget them.
We must not change them.
We must follow them.
They are the footsteps
  of our Ancients.

27

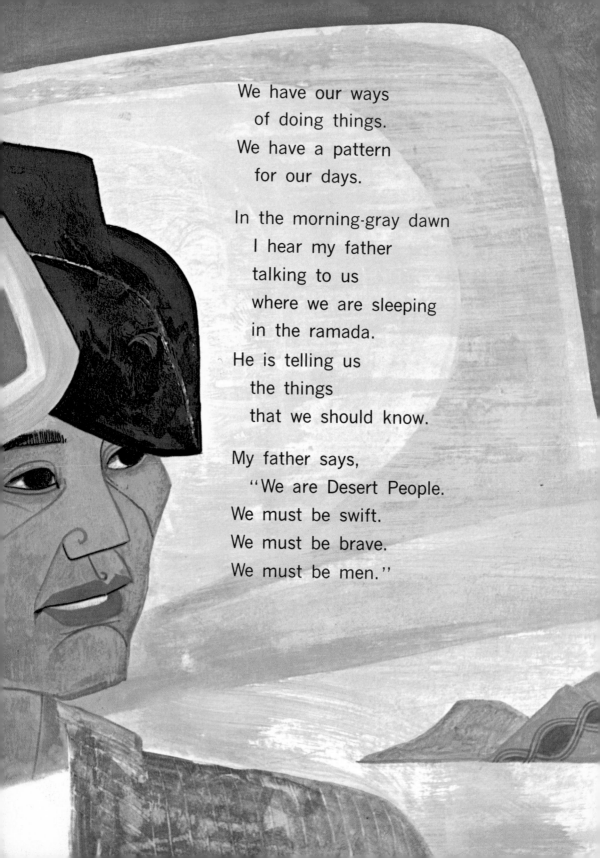

We have our ways
   of doing things.
We have a pattern
   for our days.

In the morning-gray dawn
   I hear my father
   talking to us
   where we are sleeping
   in the ramada.
He is telling us
   the things
   that we should know.

My father says,
   "We are Desert People.
We must be swift.
We must be brave.
We must be men."

"Sometimes
   we are hungry and thirsty,
   we are sunburned and tired,
   but we must meet these things
   without words
   that cry out
   to shame us."

My father says,
   "These things are not given us.
We learn to know them
   by many meetings.
Morning stands up, my sons.
Stand up to meet it.
Go forth into the dawn,
   running."

                        Ann Nolan Clark

29

# EDDIE AND HIS CATS

Eddie stopped at the fish market on his way home from school.

"Hello, Eddie," said Mr. Henderson. "What do you want? Fish heads, I'll bet."

"Right," said Eddie. "You should see the cat I have now. She's the biggest cat you ever saw. And a tortoise-shell."

"Where do you keep all the cats you bring home?" asked Mr. Henderson.

"Oh, I have a nice little pen for them," said Eddie. "My mother won't let me keep them in the house."

30

"I should think not," said Mr. Henderson. He rolled some fish heads in a paper and Eddie started home.

He hadn't gone far when he came upon a cat. The cat came near Eddie and sniffed, then it ran along with Eddie. About a block from home, Eddie looked down and there was another cat running along beside him.

"Good thing Mr. Henderson gave me a lot of fish heads," Eddie said to himself.

At the front gate Eddie found still another cat. As they followed him around to the back of the house, Eddie thought, "I never had four cats before. This is wonderful!"

Then Eddie thought that he had better not say anything about the cats to the family.

Eddie put the three cats into the pen with the big tortoise-shell cat. He emptied the paper of fish heads into the pen and the cats fell upon them.

"Eddie," his mother called out when he went indoors, "you smell of fish. Go and wash your hands. I am going to get rid of that cat, and I don't want you ever to bring any more cats home."

Eddie went off to wash his hands.

In the middle of the night Eddie was awakened by a terrible noise. The cats were screeching and wailing. He heard his father's footsteps in the hall. Then he heard a window open. Then—*splash*! He knew that his father had thrown water on the cats. "Meow!" said a cat, and then all was quiet. Eddie fell asleep, feeling sorry for his cats.

The next morning at breakfast Eddie's father said, "Now see here, Eddie, I want you to get rid of those cats. And I want you to get rid of them today. Do you understand?"

"Can't I even keep the tortoise-shell cat?" asked Eddie.

"You may not keep the tortoise-shell, or any other cat," said his father. "We are through with cats."

"Yes, sir," said Eddie, looking very sad. "What shall I do with them?"

"I don't know," said his father. "You brought them here, so you will have to get rid of them."

Eddie found a large box in the garage and put the four cats into the box. Then he put the box in his wagon and started off. He had no idea what he would do with the cats. He pulled his wagon along until he met a boy about his own age.

"Would you like a cat?" Eddie asked.

"Sure," said the boy.

"I'll give you one," said Eddie. "They're in my wagon. Which one do you want?"

The boy looked them over and then he said, "I would like the black-and-white one."

"Okay!" said Eddie. He picked up the black-and-white cat and handed it to the boy.

"Thanks," said the boy. "I'm going to call it Patches."

Eddie went off with his wagon and the three cats that were left. He hadn't gone far when he came upon a man who was repairing his front step. Eddie stopped. "Would you like to have a nice cat?" he asked.

"Don't want any cats," said the man.

"My father won't let me keep them," said Eddie in a sad voice. "And they are very nice."

"Don't want any, thanks," said the man.

"It doesn't cost much to feed one cat," said Eddie. "It doesn't cost anything if you get fish heads from the fish market."

"Don't want any," said the man.

"Oh, dear!" said Eddie. "How would you feel if you were a nice cat and nobody wanted you?"

"Okay!" said the man. "You win. Put the cat down and get out of here."

Eddie lifted the big tortoise-shell cat out of the box and set her down beside the man. "She's the prettiest cat I ever saw," he said, "and the biggest too. I think you'll like her."

The man grunted, and Eddie and his wagon rattled off with the two remaining cats.

35

At the next corner he met Billy Porter. "Hi, Bill!" Eddie shouted. "Want a nice cat?"

Billy looked into the box. "What's the matter with them?" he asked.

"Nothing is the matter with them."

"Well, why are you giving them away?"

"Pop won't let me keep them," said Eddie. "He doesn't appreciate cats. Which one do you want?" ·

"Don't want any," said Billy. "My father doesn't appreciate cats either."

"Couldn't you take just one?"

"Well," said Billy, "I'll see. Give me the gray one with white paws. He's pretty."

Eddie handed over the gray cat with the white paws. "You won't be sorry," he said. "He's a nice cat."

"Well," said Billy, "I don't know whether my father will let me keep him."

At the next corner Eddie met Kenny Roberts. "Hi, Ken!" Eddie called out. "Would you like to have a nice cat?"

"No, thanks," said Kenny. "We already have two cats."

"Oh," said Eddie, and he went on with the one cat. Soon he met Ellen. "Oh, Ellen!" he sang out. "How would you like a nice cat?"

"I don't think so," said Ellen. "I would like it, but I don't think my family would."

"Just try it overnight," said Eddie.

Ellen took the cat. "All right," she said, "but I don't think they will like it."

Eddie ran all the way home with the wagon rattling behind him. Suddenly he stopped and stared at the doorstep.

Eddie could hardly believe his eyes, for there sat the great big tortoise-shell cat with the black-and-white cat. They were busy licking themselves.

"Well!" said Eddie. "How did you get here?"

The cats went on licking.

Just then Eddie looked up the street. He saw Billy Porter coming with a cat in his arms. Eddie was not surprised when Billy called out, "Didn't I tell you? My father doesn't appreciate cats."

While Eddie sat in his wagon looking at the cats, Ellen arrived. "I'm sorry, Eddie," she said, "but my family won't let me keep this cat."

"Not even overnight?" wailed Eddie.

"No," said Ellen. And she placed the cat in the box. "I have to run home," she said. "I have to mind the baby. Good-by."

"'By!" said Eddie. "I sure think I have a hard life."

And Eddie began to wonder whether he was as fond of cats as he had thought.

*Carolyn Haywood*

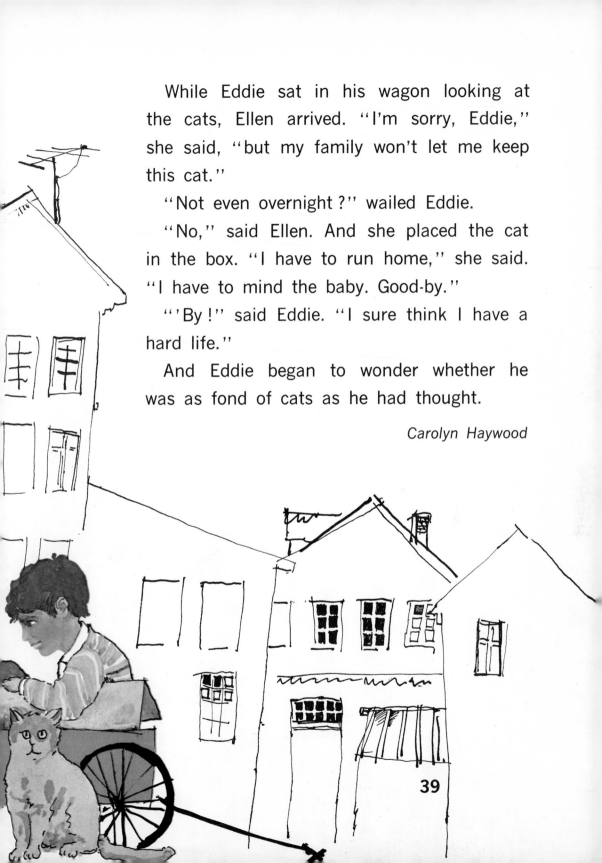

**39**

# Snow in the City

Snow is out of fashion,
  But it still comes down
To whiten all the buildings
  In our town;
To dull the noise of traffic;
  To dim each glaring light
With star-shaped feathers
  Of frosty white.
And not the tallest building
  Halfway up the sky;
Or all the trains and busses,
  And taxis scudding by;
And not a million people,
  Not one of them at all,
Can do a thing about the snow
  But let it fall!

*Rachel Field*

40

# Snowstorm Before Christmas

"Oh, boy! It'll snow! And tomorrow is Christmas!" Eddie flipped his furry cap into the air, missing Mom's reading lamp. It landed among the potted plants Willa Mae was watering.

"Cut it, Ed!" she cried. "And be sure to stay right with Jason. Mom said for you boys to be home before the snow gets bad."

"Okay, we'll make it home," Jason promised. "It isn't snowing yet. Come on, Eddie. I've got our money all counted."

Eddie slammed the front door. They clattered down the stairs fast.

"Is there enough money for the lamp shade, Jay?" Eddie asked to make sure. "And what will we get for Willa Mae?"

"We'll find something. There'll be enough."

It wasn't long before they caught their first sight of the fountain in the park.

"It's frozen!" Eddie gasped. He pulled Jason toward it. The water in the fountain must have frozen while it was still bubbling down. Now the statue animals—the turtles, frogs, and swans—had frozen into strange, icy shapes. It was lovely, like fairyland.

"Hm . . . snow's starting," Jason said, sniffing the air. A few flakes were blowing lightly over the ice. He looked up at the gray, tumbling sky. "We'd better get downtown for our shopping," he said.

43

They went chasing and running along the Parkway till they came to Market Street.

"Gee, it IS snowing now," Jason said. "We'll hurry along, the dime store's just a block away . . . shouldn't take us long."

The store was cozy warm, and everything sparkled for Christmas. There were games and moving toys, candies and Christmas trimmings, and a lady was putting snow spray on a Christmas tree. The pet department had parakeets, fish, and turtles. Eddie wanted to see it all.

When they came to buy Mom's lamp shade, there were ever so many to choose from—big ones and little ones, all colors and shapes. They were expensive, too, Jason said, and most of them were only made of paper!

Finally they bought an inexpensive pink one. Eddie carried the package high above his head. It mustn't get squashed among the many shoppers.

"Let's get a goldfish for Willa Mae, please, Jay, she'll love it!" Eddie dragged Jason back to the pets. They had to laugh, when the clerk chased their chosen fish with his little net. Plop! It landed safely in a small waxed carton, with water and a water plant. Jay counted out fifty-five cents.

"We're set, let's go," said Jason. "We've got enough money left for the bus fare home and for one of those snow sprays. I do want one of those!"

"The only spray left is pink, boys," the saleslady told them. They decided it would do—Mom likes pink. With their three packages they made for the street door.

"Oh, NO!" Jason cried. The sidewalk and street were now covered with thick snow. Every moment more was piling up. The street lights were on, shining dimly through the snow. Cars jammed the street.

Eddie followed Jason to their bus stop. A crowd of snowy cold people stood waiting there. Eddie and Jason started to wait too. No bus came, only more and more people, and more and more snow.

"There'll be no buses! We'll have to walk," Jason told Eddie. "Mom will get to worrying if we don't show up soon. I'll have to carry the fish box inside my coat."

Jason's jacket wouldn't zipper. He held the two fronts together as they began the long, slow walk home, facing wind and snow.

47

"This lamp shade is getting soaked!" Eddie shouted into the wind. It was hard to steer the large light package which the wind was blowing about like a kite. Sometimes they walked backwards to rest their faces from the stinging, blinding snow.

"You're shivering, Jay," Eddie said.

"The goldfish has started to leak," Jay said. "Come on, Ed, we've got to keep moving. It's not letting up any."

Their hands hurt with cold, so did their faces and feet. The way home seemed so much longer than it had before.

At last they turned onto their block. Snow lay piled high over the front steps. They tumbled inside the apartment-house door.

"You're home!" came Mom's voice from upstairs. Eddie felt his eyes sting with tears to hear Mom's gentle, welcoming voice. Yes, they were HOME!

"No buses . . ." Jason started to explain, and then they both flopped down on chairs in the kitchen, worn out.

"You poor kids, tell me later. Willa Mae, quick!" Mom called. "Some hot cocoa for the boys, and help them off with their things while I find dry clothes. They're wet through and almost frozen!"

Eddie's face was warming up enough to smile. Sometimes it felt good to be fussed over by Willa Mae and Mom. The sweet, hot cocoa was delicious. Eddie was beginning to feel like new.

Then he remembered his package, and the warm feeling drained out of him with a rush. How would he ever fix up that lamp shade by tomorrow morning? As soon as Mom and Willa Mae had gone back into the parlor to watch TV, he dashed out on the landing where he had left it. The lamp shade was badly damaged. And they had used up almost all their money!

"Never you worry," Jay said. "First we'll dry it. I think I might just be catching an idea how we can make it look nice. Help me find the big pickle jar for the goldfish, Ed."

They looked everywhere for Mom's big pickle jar. It was on the shelf, half full of dill pickles. But what to do with the pickles?

"Eat 'em!" Eddie said. "Hand me some."

Never had pickles tasted so delicious, and never had he eaten so many! They poured the goldfish and water plant into the clean jar. Now to hide it under their bed. The damaged lamp shade had dried, but oh, it looked so water-stained and battered, even worse than Mom's old one!

"Let's try this." Jason brought out the can of snow spray. He shook it. They sprayed just a little of the pink snow on the shade.

"It works!" Eddie shouted.

"Shush, they'll hear you! Now you spray while I turn it slowly."

There, it was done. Pink fluff covered all the ugly stains. The lamp shade looked as pretty as new. They would put it on the lamp first thing tomorrow morning. Then Eddie heard the TV program coming to an end. He whisked the shade into their bedroom.

When Eddie woke up on Christmas morning, Mom and Willa Mae were already up. He shook Jay.

"Wake up! Now's our chance!" Eddie whispered. "Grandma's here and they're all in the kitchen getting dinner ready."

Jason jumped out of bed. He fastened the new pink shade on Mom's old reading lamp. Eddie tiptoed into the parlor carrying the pickle jar carefully. Then they heard Mom's footsteps and flew back into bed, pulling the covers up high.

"Eddie and Jason! Have you seen the pickles?" she called. There she stopped—not another word! They heard the kitchen door close again. Had Mom seen it? Sure she had! Eddie crept deeper under the blankets to muffle his giggles.

But even there delicious smells reached his nose—stuffed turkey and sweet-potato pie, and the piney smell of their Christmas tree. Soon his uncles and their families would arrive. Tingles of happiness ran all over him in shivers, fit to burst.

"Merry Christmas!" Eddie shouted.

Christmas had come.

*Candida Palmer*

# Can You Puzzle It Out ?

Inside each square you will find clues to a word. Under each square is another clue to help you puzzle out the answer.

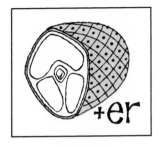 

a tool        something special        a vegetable

not large        a game        a floor covering

## Here are three harder ones !

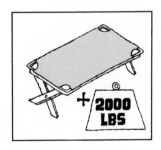 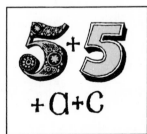 

a cloth        a state        an ice cream flavor

# For Your Very Own

In "The Wonderful Visit to Miss Liberty," Bonnie and William learned that the Statue of Liberty is a symbol for freedom. A symbol is something which stands for or represents something else. A flag is also a symbol. Its design can stand for many things.

How many of these flags do you know? What do you think their designs represent?

You can design a flag. You might like to design a flag for your school, your class, your club, or your family.

Perhaps you might have another idea for a flag. Think carefully about what you want your design to represent. After you have designed your flag, be prepared to tell your classmates about it and what it represents.

# OTHER PLACES, OTHER PEOPLE

## 2

# The Flute Player of Beppu

Far away in Japan is a city on the Inland Sea called Beppu.* Of all the good people there, no one was so admired as the flute player. When the flute player put his flute to his lips, out came such strange, sweet music that everyone stopped to listen.

By day, the flute player wandered up into the hills above the city, along the country roads past green rice fields and neat farmers' cottages. Or he followed the wide roadway along the sea that led to the harbor, busy with ships loading and unloading.

* Be'pü

**58**

At night, when Beppu was a city of a thousand lights, the flute player roamed through the narrow, winding streets. Often he stopped outside a bright teahouse.

Wherever the fluté player went, people loved the music he played.

One of the many people who waited each day for the flute player was a small boy named Sato-san.* Sato-san lived on his father's farm up in the green hills above the city. He knew well the country sounds—of birds, of crickets, the songs of farmers as they planted or harvested rice. But best of all he loved the sound of the flute player's flute.

\* Sät'ō-sän

Each day Sato-san would stand by the side of the road until he heard the strange sweet music of the flute. Then, because he was shy, he would hide behind bushes, listening to the wonderful music until the flute player had gone on down the road.

One summer day Sato-san was walking along the road in front of his father's house. His wooden shoes sent small puffs of dust into the air. He stumbled and fell. And there beside him on the road he saw what looked like a long piece of bamboo. It was a flute! Gently he picked it up. His fingers covered the holes of the flute one by one.

**60**

"What a lucky boy I am," he said to himself. He put the flute to his lips and out came a pure sweet tone. He smiled. "I shall learn to play you. And you and I will travel throughout the country, just like the flute player and his flute."

Sato-san put the flute inside his kimono. "No one will know about you until I can play you," he said.

Now that very morning the flute player's wife had looked out of her house with its clean floors and sliding doors. There in the garden were four new morning-glory blossoms. They looked so fresh and lovely in the morning sun that she wanted the flute player himself to see them. Away she went to find him. At last she saw him talking to a farmer in the road.

"Come," she said. "My morning-glory blossoms are out for the first time. You must see them in the morning sun!"

The flute player followed his wife home. Once in the garden, the two of them sipped tea and admired the four beautiful new morning glories.

Some time later, the flute player reached into the folds of his kimono for his flute. It was gone.

"My flute!" he cried. "Where is my flute?" He couldn't remember playing it that morning. He searched the house from floor to roof, but the flute was nowhere to be found.

He hurried out into the streets of Beppu, asking everyone, "Have you seen my flute?" Each one shook his head.

The flute player hurried down to the harbor. Three ships were in, and men were busy loading and unloading. "Have you seen my flute?" the flute player cried. The men shook their heads.

The sun was high when the flute player set out for the country lanes. At farmhouses, in the rice fields, he stopped people to ask, "Have you seen my flute?" But everyone shook his head—all but one small boy. And nobody saw *him.* For Sato-san had already scampered toward home.

By the time the flute player started sadly back to the city, the boy had rushed through the front yard and was lying on the hay in his father's barn.

Sato-san brought out the flute he had found. His eyes shone. "You are *my* flute," he said. "I will learn to play such music that everyone will stop to listen. *I* found you. You belong to me."

Then Sato-san remembered how sad the flute player had looked. What if the flute he had found belonged to the flute player?

What would the flute player do without his flute and his music? Would he wander through the streets, still looking for his flute, stopping in bright teahouses, and asking, "Have you seen my flute?"

Sato-san looked again at the flute. "I found you," he said. "I will take good care of you. I will never lose you."

But the more Sato-san looked at the flute, the more he thought of the flute player. And the more he thought, the more Sato-san knew what he must do.

He heard his mother call. Slowly he got up and, with the flute in his hands, he walked into the yard. His mother was waiting for him.

"I shall be late for supper," he said. "There is something I must do, for I have found a flute which may belong to the flute player."

His mother threw up her hands. "What? You have found the flute player's flute?"

"Now," said Sato-san, "I must return it."

So, just as the sun moved down behind the high hills, Sato-san started for the edge of town. He carried the flute ever so gently. By the time he reached the flute player's house, the first stars were twinkling in the evening sky. The lights of the town were beginning to go on. Sato-san pushed open the gate and called out, "Flute-player-san! Flute-player-san!"

The door slid open and there, bowing before Sato-san, was the flute player's wife. She asked him to come in. He took off his shoes and placed them outside the door next to the shoes of the flute player and his wife. Then he stood up and said, "I think I've found the flute player's flute!"

The flute player's wife threw up her hands. "You have found the flute player's flute!" she cried. She scurried into another room, calling, "He has found the flute! the flute!" Sato-san followed her.

The flute player was sitting by a low table, chopsticks in hand, and a bowl of rice before him. He looked up, surprised and happy. "Come in," he said.

Shyly Sato-san looked at the man whom everyone loved and admired. His eyes were kind. Slowly Sato-san reached inside his kimono and brought out the flute.

"Ah," said the flute player. "My flute!" He put the flute to his lips. Out came the strange sweet music that Sato-san knew and loved so well.

The flute player's wife brought in a bowl of steaming rice and placed it on the table. She pushed a cushion up to the table and bowed to Sato-san.

"Please sit down," she said. Sato-san sank down on the cushion. Then the flute player and Sato-san together picked up their chopsticks and began to eat.

No one spoke for a long time. At last Sato-san said, "I found the flute in the road in front of my father's farm."

"Ah, so," said the flute player.

"I didn't return it right away," said Sato-san. "I didn't know it was yours." He looked up. The flute player was watching him quietly. "I didn't want it to be yours," said Sato-san. "I wanted it for myself."

The flute player's eyes grew wide.

"I have heard your music many times. And I love it," Sato-san said. "I wanted the flute so that I could learn to play such music as you do."

The flute player set down his rice bowl. "And why do you like my music?"

"Because," said Sato-san, "it makes me think of cherry trees, pink as a sea shell in the spring, of green damp rice fields in the early morning, of shining ships in the harbor, and of woodsmoke in the autumn."

The flute player smiled. "I was once young like you. When I heard the old flute player's music, it made me, too, think of all the things of which you speak. It was my greatest dream to be a flute player."

Sato-san said shyly, "It is mine, too."

"Then we shall see," said the flute player. "Because you are a truthful boy, and because you love the music of my flute, I shall teach you how to play it. You will come with me every day. We will go up into the hills above the city along the country roads. We will follow the wide roadway along the sea that leads to the harbor. And at night we will go through the narrow streets of the town."

"Oh!" cried Sato-san, his brown eyes shining. "When will you teach me?"

"Tomorrow morning we will begin," said the flute player.

That night, before Sato-san went to sleep, he shut his eyes and saw himself wandering with the flute player throughout the countryside. That night he dreamed that one day he would play the flute himself.

And so it happened. If you should ever travel to that far-off city and hear a flute tune—strange and sweet—you will know that you are listening to Sato-san, the boy who became the flute player of Beppu.

*Kathryn Gallant*

71

Broken and broken
again on the sea, the moon
so easily mends.

*Chosu*

Over the wintry
forest, winds howl in a rage
with no leaves to blow.

*Soseki*

72

Ere yet the sun is high,
All blue the iris blossoms wave,
The color of the sky.

*Unknown Japanese poet*

At dawn
The pink clouds,
Like hundreds of crabs,
Creep from the hollows of heaven.

*Akiko Yosano*

**73**

# Great Day in Ghana

Kwasi* cut himself a new piece of soap from the bar on the shelf, picked up his bucket and walked across the village to the tap. Several boys were already there with their buckets. They soaped themselves till they were covered with white foam from head to toe, scrubbing at their bodies with handfuls of dried grass. Kwasi had never seen them work so hard at their baths before. They wanted to be extra clean, for it was the eve of Independence Day. Tomorrow, March 6th, was a great day of celebration. It was Ghana's Independence Day.

* Kwäs'ē

74

"I am going to Accra* tomorrow," said Kwasi. "I am going right to Accra on the mammy lorry to see my grandmother."

The boys looked at him with round eyes. "You might get lost. You are too small to go so far," said one of them.

"Oh, I've been before," Kwasi boasted.

"You will miss the celebrations here," said another boy. "You will miss the feasting and drumming and dancing."

"It will be better still in Accra," said Kwasi. "There will be fireworks."

"Listen," said the boys. "The drumming is starting already."

* Äk rä'

"It is Kofi,"* said one of the boys. "He has started already. He would drum all day and all night if he could."

"He is the best drummer in the village," said Kwasi.

"He is the best in all the villages around," said another boy.

They began to move their feet to the sound of the drumming. Blobs of soap flew this way and that like blossoms on a windy day.

* Kō'fē

76

Kwasi had finished his bath. He walked back to his house.

"Kwasi, is that you?" asked his mother. She was cooking at the fire beside the house. She had a pot of soup and a big pan of rice. Kwasi sniffed the soup hungrily.

"Come, it is time to eat," his mother called. "Here Amma,* take this to your father." Amma was Kwasi's sister. She took the pot of food from her mother and went over to the men sitting under the trees. Kwasi and the rest of the children crowded around the big pot.

* Ä'mä

All this time the drumming went on. Sometimes it was fast and sometimes it was slow, but it went on and on like a great heart beating. Quite a number of people were dancing now. That was how the drumming was. It made people dance even if they didn't want to. It pulled them like a strong cord. Soon the whole village would be dancing. It pulled at the children too. They made a little group of their own just outside the circle of grown-up people, watching how they moved their feet and their bodies and trying to dance in the same way. They danced until they were tired.

It was long after dark when Kwasi crept onto his mat, and went to sleep.

When Kwasi woke it was still dark, but there was a faint glow in the sky and he knew that the sun would soon rise. He got up and washed his face. He must hurry. The mammy lorry would get to his village soon after sunrise. He chewed a bit of stick to clean his teeth. It tasted sharp and clean. The rest of the family were still asleep.

Kwasi walked across the village. The road ran along at the end of the village and, as Kwasi walked towards it, he heard the mammy lorry and he began to run. The green lorry drew up at the side of the road. Somebody let the flap down and Kwasi climbed into the lorry. It was already full of people and all of them had baskets and bundles. Kwasi managed to find a place to sit.

The lorry started off, swaying a little as it went down the road. The driver began to sing and everybody joined in. Kwasi did not know the words of the song, but he beat his feet on the floor in time.

At last, after the long ride, the lorry reached Accra and everybody jumped down. Kwasi walked towards his grandmother's house. The streets were full of people.

His grandmother lived in the old part of the town. She was a cake seller. She fried cakes for the people passing by to eat.

When he saw his grandmother, Kwasi began to run. "Grandmother," he called out. "Grandmother, I have come."

Kwasi's grandmother sat on her wooden stool behind her fires. She did not get up, for she hardly ever moved from her stool.

"Kwasi, my grandson," she said. "Let me look at you. You have grown a lot in a year."

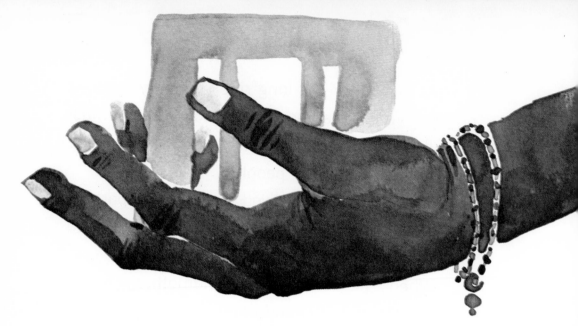

"Grandmother," said Kwasi quickly, "are you coming to the celebrations?"

"I must make cakes, Kwasi. People still want to eat on Independence Day. I am too old for singing and dancing. Such things are for young people. You go, Kwasi, and in the evening I will meet you at the Independence Arch. We will watch the fireworks together."

"But how shall I find the Independence Arch?" asked Kwasi.

"You can see it from faraway. It is shaped like this," said Kwasi's grandmother. Quickly she made the arch with a piece of batter and dropped it in the hot fat to cook. When it was cooked she gave it to Kwasi.

"The arch is like this. Anyone will show you the way. Take some more cakes. Take as many as you like." Some people were coming down the street, dancing as they came.

"But Grandmother . . ." began Kwasi. Before he had time to say any more the people closed round him in a circle, pressing against him so that he had to dance with them. "Good-by, Grandmother," he called.

Kwasi looked around. There was a low wall close by and he sat down to get his breath.

"You dance well for such a small boy," said a voice beside him. A boy a little older than Kwasi was also sitting on the wall.

"My name is Kojo,"* said the boy. "I will stay with you. You might get lost by yourself."

"I won't get lost," said Kwasi, taking out his grandmother's cakes. "I won't get lost because I've got this cake to help me find my way."

"Independence Arch," cried the boy. "That's where I'm going. I will show you the way." The two boys wandered down the street, eating the rest of the cakes.

"What's that coming down the street?" asked Kwasi. "I can hear drumming."

* Kō'jō

84

It was a parade. First came a group of dancers, their bodies painted with white patterns. After them was a man carrying a huge drum on his shoulders, and then another with an enormous red umbrella trimmed with gold. In the shade of the umbrella walked a chief. He was a very old chief, and he walked slowly.

"It is one of the chiefs," said Kojo. "Many chiefs are gathering here to watch the drumming and dancing."

**85**

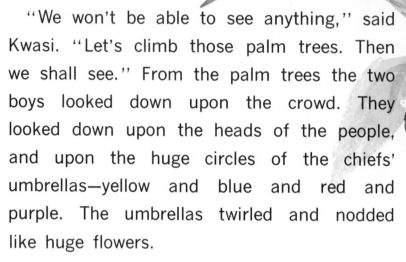

"We won't be able to see anything," said Kwasi. "Let's climb those palm trees. Then we shall see." From the palm trees the two boys looked down upon the crowd. They looked down upon the heads of the people, and upon the huge circles of the chiefs' umbrellas—yellow and blue and red and purple. The umbrellas twirled and nodded like huge flowers.

"My arms are tired and I am thirsty," said Kwasi in a little while, "and I must get to Independence Arch before nightfall."

86

He picked a coconut and slid down the tree. The boys shared the sweet coconut milk as they walked. Finally Kojo said, "Look!"

Kwasi looked around. Ahead of him was a long grassy slope and at the top was the Independence Arch, shaped just like the cake that Grandmother had given him. Hundreds of people were gathered on the grass around the arch, waiting for the fireworks.

"Come on, Kojo, I've got to find my grandmother," called Kwasi over his shoulder. It was Grandmother who saw Kwasi first.

"Here you are, Kwasi," she said. "So you found your way. You didn't get lost. Have you seen the dancing and the drumming?"

"Oh yes," said Kwasi. "This is my new friend, Grandmother. His name is Kojo. He helped me find my way."

Grandmother and the two boys sat on the grass. While they waited, they ate the cakes which Grandmother had brought them. The sky above them grew dark and the stars came out. A cool breeze blew in from the sea. A hush fell on the murmuring voices.

**87**

Suddenly there was a bang that made Kwasi hold his ears. A rocket shot into the sky and burst into scarlet stars. For a moment they hung in the sky, then they floated gently towards the earth.

"Is it magic?" whispered Kwasi.

"It is not magic," said his grandmother, "it is the start of the fireworks."

Kwasi stared into the sky above him. "Independence Day," he whispered. "It is a great day indeed when there are red blossoms in the night sky."

*Geraldine Kaye*

# The Sun's Travels

The sun is not a-bed when I
At night upon my pillow lie;
Still round the earth his way he takes,
And morning after morning makes.

While here at home, in shining day,
We round the sunny garden play,
Each little Indian sleepy-head
Is being kissed and put to bed.

And when at eve I rise from tea,
Day dawns beyond the Atlantic Sea,
And all the children in the West
Are getting up and being dressed.

*Robert Louis Stevenson*

**89**

# The Skating Race

"Yelle,* are you asleep?" whispered Bouke†
to his brother. There was a streak of white
moonlight on the floor. Outside, everything
was cold and white. But here in bed it was
nice and warm.

"Did you hear the news?" whispered
Bouke. "They need three horses to pull the
snowplow. The snow has never been so thick,
but the ice on the canal hasn't either."

* Yel′e          † Bü′ke

90

Yelle just wanted to sleep. There had been far too much talk the last few days—talk about the snow, the ice, whether it would hold long enough. But he was as proud as the others of "their" race.

He was proud of the dangerous track which covered more than a hundred miles along the frozen canals, which went right through the "eleven old towns," across wind-swept lakes, past tiny villages and lonely farmhouses. Yet skaters must push on through the icy winter darkness. Oh, how he longed to be one of them, to be old enough! Perhaps Auke,* his brother. . . .

But now that the snow was so thick, how could they possibly clear the track and make it fit for skating?

When the boys came down for breakfast, the kettle was singing on the stove and there was frost on the windows. The radio was on. There was special news about the race. Helpers would be needed to clear the track, and school children were to have a holiday so that they could help.

* Ou'ke

"Hurrah," shouted Bouke, "just give me a broom!" But Yelle sat there quietly. Auke got up and left the room without a word. Yelle followed him with his eyes. Bouke thought, "There is something the matter with Auke, and Yelle knows what it is."

A minute later Auke poked his head inside again. "I am going over to Tabe's,"* he said.

Tabe worked at Farmer Terpstra's,† next door. He was the best skater of the village. Tabe was big and strong and very fast. But Auke had a better style. They skated a lot together, but only Tabe went in for races. He had won seven medals already. But he hadn't got the Eleven Towns Cross yet. Would he this year? Everybody knew he had put his name in the race.

\* Ta'be        † Terp'stra

The winner of the Eleven Towns Cross is a hero. At school the picture of the last winner hung just under the picture of the Queen. Fancy, thought Bouke, our Tabe hanging underneath the Queen!

The boys pulled on warm coats and pulled their caps down over their ears. As they went outside, Yelle swung the snow shovel over his shoulder and Bouke picked up a broom. They walked down the snowy path. It was bitter cold. The breath came out of their mouths in little white clouds. They headed for the canal.

That evening Bouke was more quiet. He was tired from sweeping away all that snow, and he was unhappy about Yelle. It was just as if Yelle was hiding something and it made him very quiet. Mother was quiet too. She asked about Auke only once.

"Auke is helping Farmer Terpstra now because Tabe is away," Bouke answered. "He will stay there tonight and all day tomorrow."

Yelle turned on the radio for the news. "From all over the country skaters have come to the Eleven Towns Race: two hundred and seven for the race, more than five thousand to skate along after them. The town of Leeuwarden,* where they will start before daybreak, is now filled. No more rooms are to be had, and many people will have to sit up all night. All racers must be checked by a doctor. The bodies of the racers must be well covered against the cold. Cream on the face. . . ."

"Bedtime," said Father. "It will be an early day tomorrow."

* Lāou'wärd'n

**94**

The alarm clock rattled. It must be early morning, but it was still pitch black. In a flash, Yelle remembered: they are off, the skaters . . . in the dark . . . finding their way across the ice with torches, stumbling over ice that sticks up in some places, falling in the cracks they can't see! The first few hours are hardest, he knew, when the skaters try to pass each other, all black shadows in a hurry, when they fall and others pile up on top of them.

After milking, when Yelle went outside, the icy wind almost stopped his breath. Then he saw the sun rising and he felt better. Soon the skaters would be able to see.

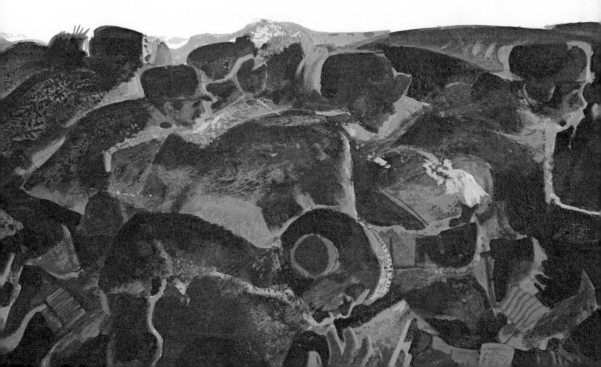

After the children finished their chores, Father asked them, "Shall we drive to the village, to see if there is any news yet?" The boys scrambled into the front seat of the truck beside Father.

The village was all astir. The streets were crowded with people. "When will the first skaters be here?" asked Father.

"Not before eleven," said the head of the village skating club. He was one of the six men who would later sit at the checking point. They would stamp the cards which showed what time each skater had arrived.

Yelle went onto the canal. Suddenly he heard cheering.

"Tabe has almost caught up with the leading group," he heard. "But there is somebody else with him—no one knows who."

Someone turned to ask Yelle, "I haven't seen your Auke all day. Isn't he with you?"

Yelle felt himself getting red in the face. He hurried away, pretending he hadn't heard.

"There they are," yelled a boy.

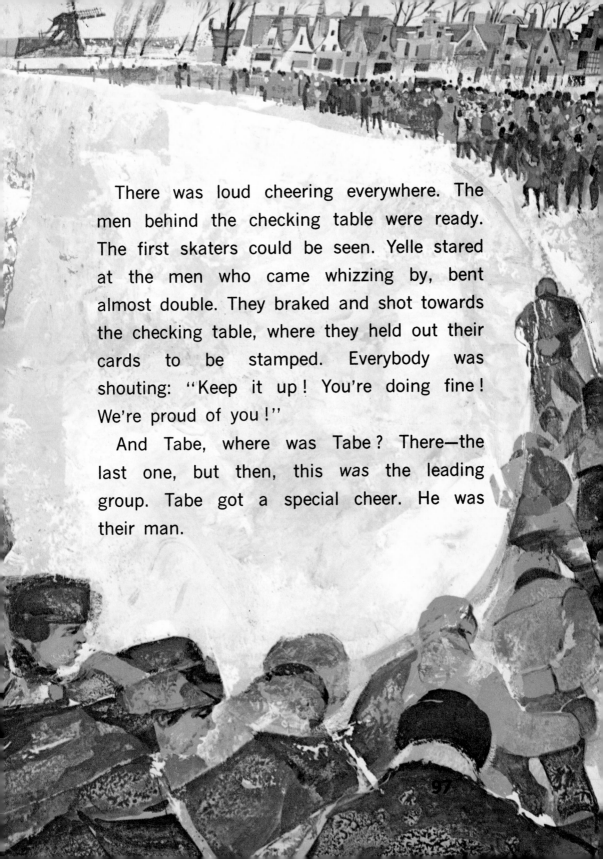

There was loud cheering everywhere. The men behind the checking table were ready. The first skaters could be seen. Yelle stared at the men who came whizzing by, bent almost double. They braked and shot towards the checking table, where they held out their cards to be stamped. Everybody was shouting: "Keep it up! You're doing fine! We're proud of you!"

And Tabe, where was Tabe? There—the last one, but then, this *was* the leading group. Tabe got a special cheer. He was their man.

The whole village was thrilled to think their Tabe might be the winner! There he was off again, after drinking a cup of hot milk and egg. He was no longer the last one. He caught up with the numbers seven and eight, then passed them. Soon the group was out of sight.

Yelle's heart sank. He was the only one who had been watching for that other skater who should have been with Tabe and wasn't. Then he heard, "The next group is coming!"

Dare he look? Yes, there in the middle of the second group was the one he was looking for—a quiet, slim skater with a cap pulled down over his head.

All of a sudden someone shouted, "But that's Auke!" At once hundreds of people were calling his name. Yelle could not join in, there was such a lump in his throat.

"Didn't you know?" someone shouted at him. "Didn't you know that Auke was in the race?" Auke was cheered almost as much as Tabe. Tabe was a giant among skaters. But they were proud of Auke too.

Auke was off again. He was less hurried than the others, but just as fast. Everyone shouted after him. Yelle wanted to shout too, but he couldn't. He had lost his voice. His eyes smarted with tears. Yelle saw Auke speeding away. Auke hadn't even seen him.

Suddenly Yelle felt an arm around his shoulders. It was Father. "You knew it, didn't you?" Father asked.

Yelle nodded, he still could not speak. There was something in Father's voice that made him feel very happy. "It is the greatest surprise of my life," Father said.

Bouke came running towards Yelle, his face as red as a beet. Now Yelle was pleased to see him. He did not want to hide from people any more.

Suddenly news spread like wildfire: the leading group is nearing Leeuwarden, the finishing point, and only five of them are left. Their names are given, but Tabe's is not among them. Their Tabe had given up! But an unknown skater has pulled ahead from the second group. Can it be Auke?

"Come along," said Father. "We can watch the finish on television at Farmer Terpstra's."

In Farmer Terpstra's living room the family is sitting on the floor in front of the television set. There is the finish line on the screen. And there in a flash are the skaters. You can't see who they are . . . they're too close together.

There, they're drawing apart . . . that third one, can it be Auke? People are cheering and stamping in the snow. Number three passes Number two. Yelle's heart nearly bursts.

It *is* Auke, you can tell by the way he skates. Yelle sees Auke come even with Number one. There is a roar from the crowd. The unknown skater whizzes past the finish. And then they hear the winner's name, and the name of their village.

Auke is lifted shoulder high, then suddenly his face appears, filling the screen. His sweater, his cap, his eyebrows, everything is white with frost. He is still breathing hard. "I am happy," he says.

Yelle felt Father's arm around his shoulder, squeezing it. But of course it was Bouke who found the breath to shout, "Now our Auke's picture will hang underneath the Queen's!"

*Rutgers van der Loeff*

# Can You Finish The Race?

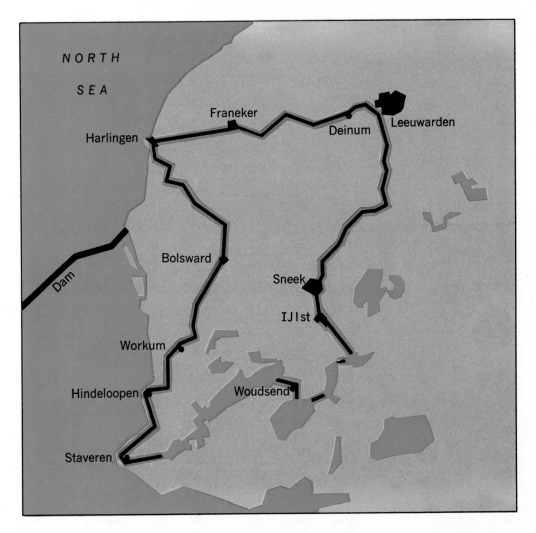

In the story you have just finished, the skaters began in Leewarden and then went to Deinum. Can you now complete the race? In what town do you think Yelle, Bouke, and Auke lived? Read the part of the story that would give you a good idea.

# An Alphabet Game

For each of the letters of the alphabet, make a sentence as follows:

<u>A</u>. My name is A_____. I come from A_____ and I sell a_____.

The lists below will help you begin.

| My name is | I come from | I sell |
|---|---|---|
| Barbara | America | hats |
| Gail | Delaware | bamboo |
| Henry | France | dill pickles |
| Alex | Hawaii | arches |
| Ellen | Brazil | fountains |
| Carol | Greece | copper |
| Fernando | Europe | goldfish |
| David | Canada | elastics |

# All About Boys and Girls

I know all about boys, I do,
And I know all about little girls, too.
I know what they eat. I know what they drink.
I know what they like. I know what they think.

And so I'm writing this to say,
Don't let children out to play.
It makes them sad. They'd rather go
To school or to the dentist. Oh,

I know they're bashful about saying
How much it hurts to be out playing
When they could go to school and spell
And mind their manners. They won't tell

How tired they are of games and toys.
But I know girls, and I know boys.
They like to sweep floors, chop the wood,
And practice being very good.

They'd rather sit and study hard
Than waste the whole day in the yard.
What good is fun and making noise?
That's not for girls! That's not for boys!

*John Ciardi*

# THE DRAGON IN THE CLOCK BOX

On Tuesday afternoon Joshua's mother went shopping and bought a new alarm clock. When she opened it, Joshua asked her if he might have the box it came in.

"Yes, Josh, if you like. What are you going to do with it?"

"Something," answered Joshua politely.

On Wednesday Joshua's mother saw that he had taken some paper tape and sealed the clock box closed again. Every slit and every corner was tightly covered. And wherever Joshua went, and whatever he did, he kept the clock box with him.

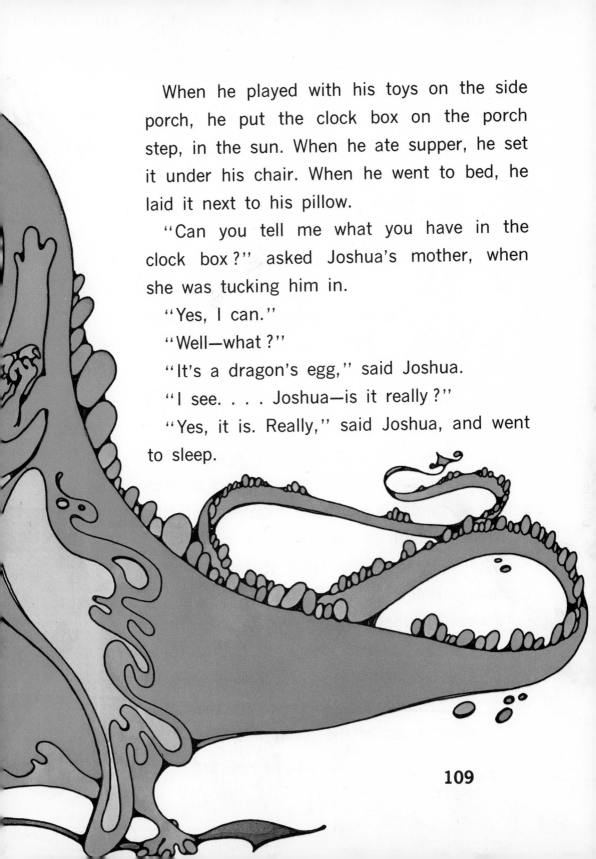

When he played with his toys on the side porch, he put the clock box on the porch step, in the sun. When he ate supper, he set it under his chair. When he went to bed, he laid it next to his pillow.

"Can you tell me what you have in the clock box?" asked Joshua's mother, when she was tucking him in.

"Yes, I can."

"Well—what?"

"It's a dragon's egg," said Joshua.

"I see. . . . Joshua—is it really?"

"Yes, it is. Really," said Joshua, and went to sleep.

On Thursday, at breakfast time, Joshua's father asked him, "How is your dragon's egg doing this morning, Josh?"

"It isn't *doing.* It's just waiting."

"What on earth is it waiting for?" asked Joshua's big sister.

"For it to be time," answered Joshua. "I would like some toast, please."

"Time to hatch, I suppose?" Joshua's sister giggled as she passed him the toast.

"Yes, time to hatch," said Joshua, without smiling even a little bit. "I would like some jam on it, please."

"I hear you have a dragon's egg in that box of yours," said Joshua's big brother when he came home from high school late in the afternoon. "How did it get there?"

"The mother dragon laid it there," said Joshua. "Before."

"Before? What do you mean, before? Before what?" asked Joshua's big brother.

"Before I sealed it up, of course," Joshua explained to him, and he picked up the clock box and went out of the room with it.

That evening Joshua's father wanted to know how any air could get into the box when it was taped shut.

"It doesn't need air yet," explained Joshua. "It just needs to be warm and quiet. Until it's hatched."

"When is it going to hatch?" asked Joshua's big brother.

"When it's ready to," Joshua told him.

"But how will you know when it's ready to?" Joshua's big sister asked him, not laughing this time.

Joshua looked at her for a minute before he spoke again.

"I don't have to know. *It* will know." And in a whisper to himself, he added, "Silly."

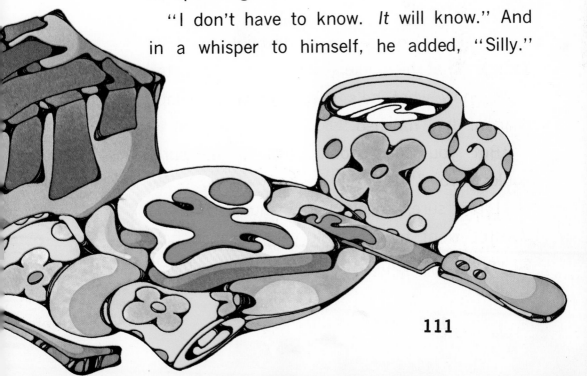

On Friday morning Joshua came down to breakfast a little bit late. He put the clock box on the table close to his plate, instead of under his chair. There was a small, neat hole cut in one corner of it.

"He's a boy dragon," Joshua said to his mother as he sat down.

"He hatched. Last night. Very late."

"How can you tell?"

"It was time."

"Did you hear it?"

"*Him*, not *it*. No, he was very quiet. But it was time, and he was ready, so I knew. So I made a hole just now. Because now he needs air."

"And now you can peek through the hole to see what he's like," said Joshua's sister.

"I know what he's like. He's like a baby dragon. Just hatched."

"But you could look, just to be sure, couldn't you?"

"I am sure," explained Joshua. "And he doesn't want me to look yet. Because he's so young. He wants to be alone for a while."

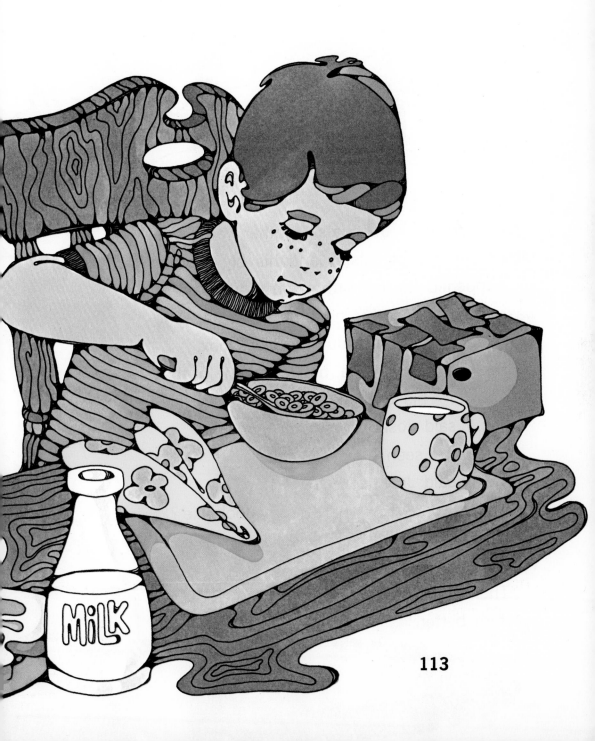

113

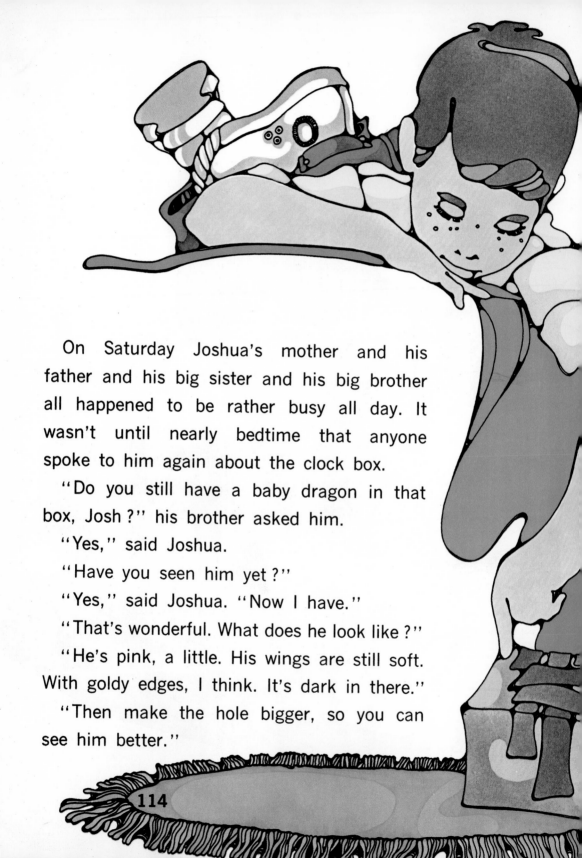

On Saturday Joshua's mother and his
father and his big sister and his big brother
all happened to be rather busy all day. It
wasn't until nearly bedtime that anyone
spoke to him again about the clock box.

"Do you still have a baby dragon in that
box, Josh?" his brother asked him.

"Yes," said Joshua.

"Have you seen him yet?"

"Yes," said Joshua. "Now I have."

"That's wonderful. What does he look like?"

"He's pink, a little. His wings are still soft.
With goldy edges, I think. It's dark in there."

"Then make the hole bigger, so you can
see him better."

"No, I can't. He wants it dark. While his wings are so soft it has to be dark."

"How do you know that, Joshua?" his mother asked him.

"It's always that way with dragons," said Joshua. "With baby-boy dragons."

On Sunday, just before lunch, Joshua told his big sister, "His name is Emmeline."

"But Josh, that's a girl's name!"

"I know, but he's a Chinese dragon. And they like to have girls' names. And his wings are hardly soft at all now."

"May I see him?"

"No, he's too shy."

"But *you* look at him."

"He's used to me."

115

Monday evening Joshua's father asked him what he had been feeding the dragon.

"They don't eat when they're little," said Joshua. "Not baby dragons. Not while their wings are still even a little bit soft."

"Well, then, what are you going to feed him when his wings get strong?"

"I won't have to feed him then," answered Joshua, and he laid his hand gently on the clock box.

And then it was Tuesday again, and Joshua came to the breakfast table without the clock box. But everyone was in a hurry to start the day, and no one noticed.

It was later, when Joshua's mother was making his bed, that she saw the clock box on the floor. The tape had been torn off and the box was open wide. It was empty.

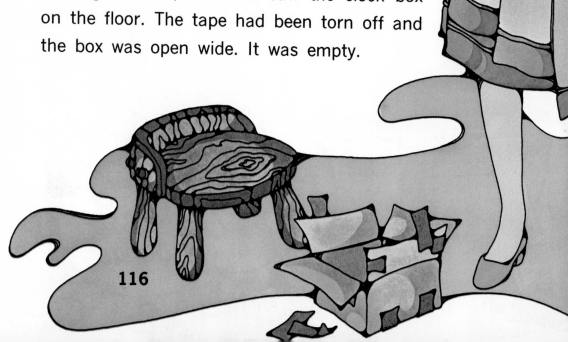

"Joshua! Your dragon's gone!"

Joshua was busy taking his marbles out of a bag, and he didn't even turn around when he answered her.

"He was big enough last night. And his wings were strong. He flew away."

"Did he really? But Josh, where could he fly to?"

Joshua turned around, then, and walked over to where the empty clock box was. He picked it up.

"Where dragons go." he said.

"This is a very good box to keep marbles in, I think. I'm going to put my marbles in it now."

And he did.

M. Jean Craig

117

# The Magic Bagpipe

Once upon a time, long ago, there was a young boy named Donald MacCrimmon. He lived with his family on the Isle of Skye, an island off the coast of Scotland.

One morning Donald went skipping across the moor. Under his arm Donald carried his chanter. He was on his way to Mister MacSkirl's house for his bagpipe lesson.

Donald did not have a bagpipe of his own. Mister MacSkirl had promised to lend him a set of bagpipes for the contest tomorrow.

The next day was the birthday of their chief. The people would gather at his castle for feasting and games. There would be a piping contest, and the winner would be named Piper to the Chief. Just thinking about that made Donald excited.

Mister MacSkirl was digging peat near his cottage when Donald got there.

"Here, boy," he called, "make yourself useful and earn your lesson."

"Yes, sir," answered Donald. He laid his chanter down carefully, then he helped stack the lumps of peat.

Donald worked hard. It was a long time before MacSkirl stopped. At last he led the way into the cottage and poured himself a cup of hot broth. He did not give any to Donald, so the boy helped himself to a drink of water from the pail in the corner. MacSkirl was a mean man. But he was a good piper, and Donald wanted to be a good piper too.

"Well, let's hear it," MacSkirl said.

Donald picked up his chanter and played the tune that he had been working on that week. When he stopped, his teacher did not say anything. Donald waited while MacSkirl got up and took his bagpipe down from the peg.

Donald tucked the bag under his arm, put the pipes over his shoulder, and blew into the blowpipe so that air filled the bag.

Then Donald played the tune again. And then he played another tune, and another. His eyes got big and his cheeks got red and his fingers flew over the holes in the chanter. How he loved the music of the bagpipe! He stamped one foot in time with the music until the very walls shook.

Suddenly Donald saw that MacSkirl was looking crossly at him. He quickly stopped piping and asked MacSkirl, "What did I do wrong, sir?"

Now, MacSkirl had just heard Donald play the pipes better than he himself could do! This made him angry. To himself he thought, "If Donald pipes tomorrow, he may win the contest instead of me."

Aloud, MacSkirl said, "I was just thinking how unhappy you'll be, Donald, but I don't have any pipes to lend you for tomorrow."

121

Donald held tight to the bagpipe and cried, "Oh, Mister MacSkirl, you promised!"

"I know, I know," said MacSkirl crossly, "but I just didn't get around to fixing my old bagpipe for you, so that's that."

He took his pipes away from Donald and turned his back on the boy. Donald picked up his chanter, put his bonnet on his head, and let himself out the door. Head hanging, he stumbled down the road.

"He promised, he promised," Donald said over and over to himself. Suddenly there was a crash of thunder. Donald noticed that it had become very dark. He started to run, but just then the rain came pouring down.

Soon it was raining so hard that Donald could hardly see. He stopped. The bridge over the river was around here somewhere.

Just then Donald heard a cry and a splash ahead of him. He ran forward, and saw a little old woman struggling in the water under the bridge. Donald scrambled down the bank, caught hold of her cloak, and pulled the old woman to safety.

"Are you all right?" he cried.

"Oh, yes, indeed! Thank you very much."

She stood there, bobbing her head and smiling at him through the rain. "And how are you?" she asked.

"Oh, fine," Donald said, "except that I'm wet, of course."

"My goodness, you are wet! How did that happen?"

Donald stared at her in surprise. "It's raining," he said.

"Why, so it is!" the old lady said. "Don't stand there talking. Come in where it's dry."

She grabbed the boy by the hand, and scurried across the moor, pulling him with her.

"Here we are!" she cried. And suddenly there was a door in front of them. She pushed it open, drew Donald in, and slammed the door against the storm.

Donald stood there panting, and brushed the wet hair out of his eyes.

"Now for some nice, hot barley broth," said the little old lady.

As she put the kettle on the fire, Donald looked at her again. She certainly was a funny little lady. She was no bigger than he, with a wide smile, a very large nose, rosy cheeks, and eyes that crinkled almost shut when she smiled. She had wispy white hair and was dressed all in green.

All in green! Why, maybe she was a fairy!

124

Donald quickly stuck his knife in the door as a magic charm against being locked up. He looked to see if the little old lady had seen him. He didn't want to hurt her feelings.

She was watching him and laughing. "Yes," she nodded. "I'm one of the 'good people,' young man, but I won't do you any harm. You did me a good turn, and I won't forget."

While she poured the broth, Donald pulled up a bench to the fireplace so that their clothes could dry.

"Isn't this cozy?" said the fairy. "But you're not very happy."

A tear ran down Donald's cheek and splashed into his cup. "I wanted to pipe in the games tomorrow, but I don't have a bagpipe," he told her.

The fairy skipped across the room to a big chest in the corner. She said to herself, "I'm quite sure I have a bagpipe here somewhere."

She looked through the chest, tossing things out over her shoulder. "Oh, goody!" she said. "Here's the bagpipe." She handed it to Donald. "Do you like it?" she asked.

"It's the handsomest set of pipes I've ever seen," Donald answered.

"You may keep it," said the fairy. "It will be your very own bagpipe, but it can be played only by you."

"Oh . . ." cried Donald.

Before he could say more, the strange little lady said, "Your clothes are dry. You had better go home now."

She pulled Donald across the floor, handed him his knife, and pushed him out the door.

"Good-by," called Donald as the door shut behind him. He hugged his new bagpipe tightly in his arms and started for home.

The next morning Donald, his sister, and his mother and father set off for the castle.

Across the road from the castle was a big open field where the games were already starting. All day there was racing and hammer throwing and other games.

Then late in the afternoon came the shout, "Pipers! Get ready!" And the contest Donald had waited for began. Piper McClure was first. Donald would be last, after O'Neil from Ireland and Mister MacSkirl.

Donald waited happily, enjoying the music. He did not notice MacSkirl a few steps away. The old man stared at the boy from under his bushy eyebrows. He had a good set of pipes himself, but Donald's pipes were the best he had ever seen.

Finally Mister MacSkirl said to Donald, "I'm sorry I didn't fix my old pipes for you."

"Oh, that's all right, sir," said Donald. "I have a bagpipe of my own now."

"So I see. But it's not a very good one. I'll tell you what I'll do. I'll trade with you."

And what did MacSkirl do then but jerk Donald's pipes from him and push his own bagpipe at the boy. Then off he went.

Donald tried to race after the man. "No, no!" he called. "Please, Mister MacSkirl. I don't want to trade."

Just then MacSkirl's name was called, and he marched out on the field.

Suddenly the boy heard a strange noise. What could it be? MacSkirl was playing. But it didn't sound like bagpipe music, it sounded like a cat fight.

128

At first the crowd listened quietly. Then someone giggled, and in a moment the whole crowd was rocking with laughter.

MacSkirl was puzzled. The pipes fell from his shaking hands. He pulled his bonnet down over his ears and fled.

Then Donald heard his own name called. He came out on the field, picked up his pipes, tucked them under his arm, and puffing out his cheeks, began to play.

The laughter died as the people turned to listen to Donald. His music was as slow and sad and lonely as a single gull wheeling in a bleak sky. It made the listeners think of the cold wind sweeping over the moor and the gray waves rolling against the rocks.

Then Donald quickened his step, and the people lifted their heads as his music changed. People began to tap their feet, to nod and smile. This music made them proud of their beautiful Isle of Skye, proud of being Scotsmen. The music swelled until everyone could feel it going through him, and the ground trembled with the warm, stirring tune.

Then Donald stopped.

For a minute there wasn't a sound, and Donald thought, "No one liked it. But I know I played well." He started to leave the field.

Then the crowd came to life with a roar. People rushed out and Donald was lifted up on someone's shoulder and carried around the field. People cheered and screamed and stamped their feet.

Finally Donald was set down on his own feet in front of the chief. The tall old man shook the boy's hand and said, "Donald MacCrimmon, that was the greatest piping I have ever heard. I am proud to call you Piper to the Chief."

131

And then Donald's parents were beside him. His father clapped him proudly on the shoulder, his mother hugged him, and his little sister jumped up and down with excitement.

Then there was feasting and drinking of toasts, and Donald had to play for dancing as the long, happy day led into a long, happy night. And the happiest person in all that celebration was Donald MacCrimmon, Piper to the Chief.

*Gerry* and *George Armstrong*

# A Piper

A piper in the streets today
Set up, and tuned, and started to play,
And away, away, away on the tide
Of his music, we started; on every side
Doors and windows opened wide,
And men left down their work and came,
And women with petticoats colored like flame,
And little bare feet that were blue with cold,
Went dancing back to the age of gold,
And all the world went gay, went gay,
For half an hour in the street today.

Seumas O'Sullivan

# FLAT STANLEY

Breakfast was ready.

"I will go wake up the boys," Mrs. Lambchop said to her husband, George Lambchop. Just then their younger son, Arthur, called from the bedroom he shared with his brother Stanley.

"Hey! Come and look! Hey!"

Mr. and Mrs. Lambchop were both very much in favor of politeness and careful speech. "Hay is for horses, Arthur," Mr. Lambchop said as they entered the bedroom. "Try to remember that."

"Pardon me," Arthur said. "But look!"

He pointed to Stanley's bed. Across it lay the enormous bulletin board that Mr. Lambchop had given the boys so that they could pin up pictures and messages and maps. It had fallen on top of Stanley.

But Stanley was not hurt. In fact he would still have been sleeping if he had not been woken by his brother's shout.

"What's going on here?" he called out cheerfully from beneath the enormous board.

Mr. and Mrs. Lambchop hurried to lift it from the bed. "Heavens!" said Mrs. Lambchop.

135

"Gosh!" said Arthur. "Stanley's flat!"

"As a pancake," said Mr. Lambchop. "Darndest thing I've ever seen."

"Let's all have breakfast," Mrs. Lambchop said. "Then Stanley and I will go see Doctor Dan and hear what he has to say."

"How do you feel?" Doctor Dan asked. "Does it hurt very much?"

"I felt sort of tickly for a while after I got up," Stanley Lambchop said, "but I feel fine now."

"Well, that's mostly how it is with these cases," said Doctor Dan.

"We'll just have to keep an eye on this young fellow," he said when he had finished checking Stanley. "Sometimes we doctors, despite all our years of training, can only wonder at how little we really know."

Mrs. Lambchop said she thought that Stanley's clothes would have to be altered by the tailor now, so Doctor Dan took Stanley's measurements and wrote them down.

Mrs. Lambchop wrote them down too.

Stanley was four feet tall, about a foot wide, and half an inch thick.

When Stanley got used to being flat, he enjoyed it. He could go in and out of rooms, even when the door was closed, just by lying down and sliding through the crack at the bottom.

Mr. and Mrs. Lambchop said it was silly, but they were quite proud of him.

Arthur tried to slide under a door too, but he just banged his head.

Being flat could also be helpful, Stanley found.

He was taking a walk with Mrs. Lambchop one afternoon when her favorite ring fell from her finger. The ring rolled across the sidewalk and down between the bars of a grating that covered a dark, deep shaft. Mrs. Lambchop began to cry.

"I have an idea," Stanley said.

He took the laces out of his shoes and another pair out of his pocket and tied them all together to make one long lace. Then he tied the end of that to the back of his belt and gave the other end to his mother. "Lower me," he said, "and I will look for the ring."

"Thank you, Stanley," Mrs. Lambchop said. She lowered him between the bars and moved him carefully up and down and from side to side, so that he could search the whole floor of the shaft.

Two policemen came by and stared at Mrs. Lambchop as she held the long lace that ran down through the grating. She pretended not to notice them.

"What's the matter, lady?" the first policeman asked. "Is your yo-yo stuck?"

"I am not playing with a yo-yo!" Mrs. Lambchop said sharply. "My son is at the other end of this lace, if you must know."

"Get the net, Harry," said the second policeman. "We have caught a cuckoo!"

Just then, down in the shaft, Stanley cried out, "Hooray!"

Mrs. Lambchop pulled him up and saw that he had the ring.

"Good for you, Stanley," she said. Then she turned angrily to the policemen.

"A cuckoo indeed!" she said. "Shame!"

"We didn't get it lady," the policemen said. "We have been hasty. We see that now."

"People should think twice before making rude remarks," said Mrs. Lambchop.

The policemen said that was a good rule and that they would try to remember it.

One day Stanley got a letter from his friend Thomas Anthony Jeffrey, whose family had moved recently to California. A school vacation was about to begin and Stanley was invited to spend it with the Jeffreys.

"Oh, boy!" Stanley said. "I would love to go!"

Mr. Lambchop sighed. "A round-trip train or airplane ticket to California is very expensive," he said. "I will have to think of some cheaper way."

When Mr. Lambchop came home from the office that evening, he brought with him an enormous brown paper envelope.

"Now, Stanley," he said. "Try this for size."

The envelope fit Stanley very well. There was even room left over, Mrs. Lambchop found, for an egg-salad sandwich made with thin bread, and a flat cigarette case filled with milk.

The next day Mr. and Mrs. Lambchop slid Stanley into his envelope, along with the egg-salad sandwich and the cigarette case full of milk, and mailed him from the box on the corner. The envelope had to be folded to fit through the slot, but Stanley was a limber boy and inside the box he straightened right up again.

Mrs. Lambchop was worried because Stanley had never been away from home alone before. She rapped on the box. "Can you hear me, dear?" she called. "Are you all right?"

Stanley's voice came quite clearly. "I'm fine. Can I eat my sandwich now?"

"Wait an hour. And try not to get overheated, dear," Mrs. Lambchop said. Then she and Mr. Lambchop cried out, "Good-by, good-by!" and went home.

Stanley had a fine time in California. When the visit was over, the Jeffreys returned him in a beautiful white envelope they had made themselves. It had red-and-blue markings to show that it was airmail, and Thomas Jeffrey had lettered it "Handle with Care" and "This End Up" on both sides.

Back home Stanley told his family that it had been handled so carefully he never felt a single bump. Mr. Lambchop said it proved that jet planes were wonderful, and so was the Post Office Department, and that this was a great age in which to live.

Stanley thought so too.

A few weeks later, however, Stanley was no longer so cheerful. People had begun to laugh and make fun of him as he passed by. "Hello, Super-Skinny!" they would shout, and even ruder things, about the way he looked.

One night Arthur Lambchop was woken by the sound of crying. In the darkness he crept across the room to Stanley's bed.

"Are you okay?" he said.

"Go away," Stanley said.

"Please let's be friends. . . ." Arthur couldn't help crying a little too. "Oh, Stanley," he said. "Please tell me what's wrong."

Stanley waited a long time before he spoke. "The thing is," he said, "I'm just not happy any more. I'm tired of being flat. I want to be my ordinary shape again, like other people. But I'll have to go on being flat forever. It makes me sick."

"Oh, Stanley," Arthur said. He dried his tears on a corner of Stanley's sheet and could think of nothing more to say.

"Don't talk about what I just said," Stanley told him. "I don't want anyone to worry. That would only make it worse."

"You're brave," Arthur said. "You really are."

He took hold of Stanley's hand. The two brothers sat together in the darkness, being friends. They were both still sad, but each one felt a *little* better than he had before.

And then, suddenly, Arthur had an idea. He jumped up and turned on the light and ran to the big storage box where toys and things were kept. He began to rummage in the box.

Arthur flung aside a football, airplane models, and lots of wooden blocks, and then he said, "Aha!" He had found what he wanted—an old bicycle pump. He held it up, and Stanley and he looked at each other.

"Okay," Stanley said at last. "But take it easy." He put the end of the long pump hose in his mouth and clamped his lips tightly about it so that no air could escape.

"I'll go slowly," Arthur said. "If it hurts or anything, wiggle your hand at me."

He began to pump. At first nothing happened except that Stanley's cheeks bulged a bit. Arthur watched his hand, but there was no wiggle signal, so he pumped on. Then, suddenly, Stanley's top half began to swell.

"It's working! It's working!" shouted Arthur, pumping away.

Stanley spread his arms so that the air could get around inside of him more easily. He got bigger and bigger. The buttons of his pajama top burst off—*Pop! Pop! Pop!* A moment more and he was all rounded out; head and body, arms and legs. But not his right foot. That foot stayed flat.

Arthur stopped pumping. "It's like trying to do the very last bit of those long balloons," he said. "Maybe a shake would help."

Stanley shook his right foot twice, and with a little *whooshing* sound it swelled out to match the left one. There stood Stanley Lambchop as he used to be, as if he had never been flat at all!

"Thank you, Arthur," Stanley said. "Thank you very much."

The brothers were shaking hands when Mr. Lambchop strode into the room with Mrs. Lambchop right behind him. "We heard you!" said Mr. Lambchop. "Up and talking when you ought to be asleep, eh? Shame on—"

"GEORGE!" said Mrs. Lambchop. "Stanley's *round* again!"

You're right!" said Mr. Lambchop, noticing. "Good for you, Stanley!"

"I'm the one who did it," Arthur said. "I blew him up."

Everyone was terribly excited and happy, of course. Mrs. Lambchop made hot cocoa to celebrate the event and several toasts were drunk to Arthur for his cleverness.

When the little party was over, Mr. and Mrs. Lambchop tucked the boys back into their beds and kissed them and then they turned out the light. "Good night," they said.

"Good night," said Stanley and Arthur.

It had been a long and tiring day. Very soon all the Lambchops were asleep.

*Jeff Brown*

# Same or Different ?

Can you complete the synonyms and antonyms below ? Remember that a synonym is a word that has the same or nearly the same meaning. An antonym is a word that has the opposite meaning.

| | |
|---|---|
| wring | _ _ _ **S** _ |
| cute | _ _ _ _ _ **Y** |
| coins | _ _ **N** _ _ |
| noisy | _ **O** _ _ |
| unite | _ _ _ **N** |
| joyful | _ _ _ _ **Y** |
| fumes | _ **M** _ _ _ |
| | |
| amused | _ **A** _ |
| wrap | _ **N** _ _ _ _ _ |
| wrong | _ _ _ _ **T** |
| girl | _ **O** _ |
| soiled | _ _ _ _ **N** |
| cute | _ _ _ **Y** |
| huge | _ **M** _ _ _ |

clean
smoke
uncover
small
happy
money
loud
join
ugly
boy
right
twist
sad
pretty

# What If ?

Stanley Lambchop was made flat when a bulletin board fell on him. Life was changed for Stanley after he became flat.

What if you became flat ?

How could it happen ?

How would your life be changed ?

What would you like about being flat ?

What wouldn't you like about being flat ?

or

What if you became round as a ball ? Or what if you became twelve feet tall and one inch wide ? What other shapes or sizes could you become ? Use the questions above to help you tell about your new shape.

The Workaday World

## City Lights

Into the endless dark
The lights of the buildings shine,
Row upon twinkling row,
Line upon glistening line.
Up and up they mount
Till the tallest seems to be
The topmost taper set
On a towering Christmas tree.

Rachel Field

154

# NIGHT WORKERS

Even as most of us sleep, there are men and women at work. In the glare of lights, in the darkness of shadows, with night all around them, they go about their jobs in places as different as fish markets and firehouses, tugboats and television stations. Life would not be as pleasant or as safe without them, but often their work and their world are unknown to day people.

The best way to meet night workers is by staying up with them. Let's suppose that it is late on a Monday afternoon, an hour or so before dark. . . .

Everywhere at this time day workers are going home, crowding the streets and highways, filling the subways and buses. In far smaller numbers, night workers have been returning to their jobs. A nurse, for example, will work until midnight in a children's ward. Then another nurse will take her place for eight hours until the day workers return.

It is now six o'clock. Work already has begun on tomorrow morning's newspaper. A rewrite man is taking notes as he talks to a reporter covering an important meeting downtown. When he hangs up, he will write a story that will appear in the newspaper's next edition about two hours from now. At other places in the city room, stories about other happenings are being prepared. Still others clatter in on teletype machines from cities throughout the country and the world.

Three floors below, printers have just started their high-speed presses rolling with the first edition. (By early tomorrow, when the sixth and last edition is run, 600 thousand newspapers will have been printed.)

Devaney

157

Monkmeyer

It is eight o'clock. Tons of vegetables have been arriving by truck and by train from farms all over the country. Now, the produce fills the sidewalks and the warehouses. Later tonight other trucks will cart it to the food stores.

**158**

It is nine o'clock. The fireman in a fire station is listening to the fire alarms that come in by bell and by loudspeaker. When an alarm is sounded for his district, he alerts the other firemen stationed here and they race for their trucks. It takes them thirty-five seconds to get under way. So far tonight, they have been out once for a fire in a kitchen and once for a false alarm. No one knows what the rest of the night will bring.

Devaney

For the past fifteen minutes, a man has been guiding a 185,000-pound jet toward the airport. With the plane now close enough to make its approach, he is giving the pilot landing instructions, "You are clear to land on Runway 4 Right. Wind 040 degrees at 17 knots. . . ."

Another plane has just left the ground. Each night, workers in this control tower help over two hundred planes to land and take off. The radar screen above the man's head gives him a picture of what is going on in the air nearby.

It is now one o'clock. Over 2,500 men and women in a huge post office work at handling the nightly flood of mail into and out of the city. By morning, some five million letters and packages will have been brought in, sorted, and sent on their way. In post offices across the country tonight, 150 thousand night workers will move 140 million pieces of mail.

Crying, hungry, and wet, a month-old baby girl has just awakened at two o'clock. So has her sleepy mother, who now is changing her and in a few minutes will feed her.

In a radio station many miles away, one man plays records, reads the news, and talks about all sorts of things on a program that is on from midnight to six o'clock in the morning. Who listens? Night workers, people who go to bed late, people who get up early, people who can't sleep, people with tiny babies. Each night about 200 thousand men and women turn on their radios to hear this program.

Over a million trucks also are on the move at this hour. When the driver finishes fastening the doors of his 50-foot tractor-trailer, he will head west to St. Louis with a load of auto parts, cloth, copper tubing, foodstuffs, and nuts and bolts. Many other trucks are still being loaded.

It is three o'clock. In a busy police station, policemen are making their reports, and people suspected of crimes are booked before they go to court.

Throughout the city over a thousand policemen are on duty. Some patrol on foot, others by car. They report in each hour by telephone or by radio. A foot patrolman walks sixteen miles on his beat each night.

At four o'clock milk has begun to move along a belt to delivery trucks outside. The driver delivers milk to stores, schools, hospitals, and hotels. The cans contain milk for baking and cooking and for machines from which milk is drawn by the glass. Earlier, workmen loaded sixty trucks that deliver milk to homes. From this one plant, almost fifty-thousand quarts are delivered every morning.

An hour or so ago, six bakers in a small bakery began mixing the bread and rolls they bake each day. Right now, they are making long, narrow rolls for sandwiches. The bakers will turn out over three thousand rolls before they are finished. Tomorrow three thousand more will be needed.

After they are shaped, the rolls are placed on wooden boards and taken to the "proofer" room where they rise for half an hour. Finally, they are placed inside the oven. After a 20-minute ride on moving trays, they arrive back ready to eat.

It is quarter to seven. Night has begun to fade. The newspaper boy has only a few more of his sixty papers to deliver. Then he will ride home, eat his breakfast, and try to get to school on time.

It is after eight. The sun is up. By bus, car, subway, and train the last of the night workers are heading for home.

Meanwhile, in a growing flood, day workers are returning. For them, for almost everyone else, the day has just begun.

*Alvin Schwartz*

# TIDES

The tide is high! The tide is high!
The shiny waves go marching by
Past ledge and shallow and weedy reach
Up the long gray lengths of shingle beach;
Like an army storming height on height
With green-blue armor and banners white
On, on they charge to the farthest line
Of scattered seaweed brown and fine—
So far, then, grumbling, back creep they,
And the tide has turned for another day.

The tide is low! The tide is low!
Weed-decked and gaunt the ledges show
With mussel shells in blues and blacks
And barnacles along their backs.
Now kelp shines like mahogany
And every rock pool brims with sea
To make a little looking glass
For sky and clouds and birds that pass.

*Rachel Field*

166

# FISHING FROM CASTLE ROCK

It was summer and the beaches were crowded. Away from the breakers little white sailboats leaned into the wind. Small motorboats rode the waves while people fished from their sides. And closer to the shore the swimmers bobbed in the blue sea.

Over all of this the Coast Guard kept watch. The Coast Guard motorboats, called cutters, were ready to go to the rescue of swimmers and overturned boats. Coast Guard helicopters were used to look for anyone who needed help faster than the boats could get there.

167

Today Bob and Jim were getting ready to report to the Sand Point Coast Guard Station for helicopter duty. Bob and Jim were in the Coast Guard. It was a job they both liked.

To make rescues at sea, a Coast Guard 'copter must carry many things. It must carry a stretcher for people who are hurt. It must carry a rescue basket which can be let down from the 'copter. People climb into the basket to be hauled from danger.

When Bob and Jim got to Sand Point, they went inside the station to report to their commanding officer. They put their things in lockers and made their beds. They put on their orange flying suits. Now they were ready for any call that came.

While Bob and Jim were on their way to the Coast Guard Station, Ron and Pete were on their way to go fishing.

"Do you have the right bait?" Pete asked.

"Sure, and the heavy poles too. I'm going after the big fish today. I want to go out to Castle Rock. That's where the best fishing is. John said we could use his boat."

It did not take long to get to Sand Point. There was Castle Rock, a big black mass with sharp points sticking up like the roof of a castle. The boys piled their fishing gear and a bag of sandwiches into John's boat.

The tide was out and the sea was calm. It took the boys about twenty minutes to row out to the rock. They found a tiny sand bar on which to beach the boat.

"You take the sea side of the rock, Pete," Ron said. "I'll take the land side. Between us we'll catch all the fish we can haul back. Take some sandwiches with you. If the big ones start biting we can't leave our poles. Those big fish can drag your gear out to sea before you can bat your eye."

Pete climbed up the rock until he found a good place to sit down. He baited his fish hook, swung his pole, and watched where the bait hit the water and started to sink. Almost at once he felt a tug on his line.

"Hey, Ron, you're right! The fish really are biting!" Pete shouted. He caught three sand dabs and a perch before he stopped to eat.

No sooner had he settled down with his sandwiches before his pole jerked again. From then on, Pete was too busy catching fish to see that the water was beginning to creep higher and higher up the rock. A chilling wind started to blow. The wind began to pull at his pole, and he had to plant his feet down hard to keep from falling into the sea.

Then Pete heard Ron's voice. He pulled in his line and put his pole between the rocks where the wind couldn't reach it. Then he started to make his way to the other side. The ocean spray made the rocks slippery. He saw for the first time how fast the tide was coming in. Pete looked around for Ron.

Just then a wave broke over the rock. Pete was soaked. He saw that his fish, his pole and his bait had been swept out to sea. A second wave splashed against the rock, covering him with white foam. Suddenly he felt a pull on the back of his jacket. Ron was dragging him up the rock. The two boys made their way to the top of Castle Rock.

The quiet tide pool at the base of the rock had turned into angry water. The boys could see pieces of wood floating. The little boat had been smashed into a hundred pieces as it crashed against the rock.

"How will we get back?" Pete cried.

"Lie down flat!" Ron answered. "Hang on! We've got to wait for the tide to go out. Then we'll swim to shore. Our boat's gone."

The boys hung onto the rocks as hard as they could. Each wave that came seemed higher than the last. They shut their eyes to keep out the stinging salt water that almost blinded them. How long could they cling to the wet, slippery rocks?

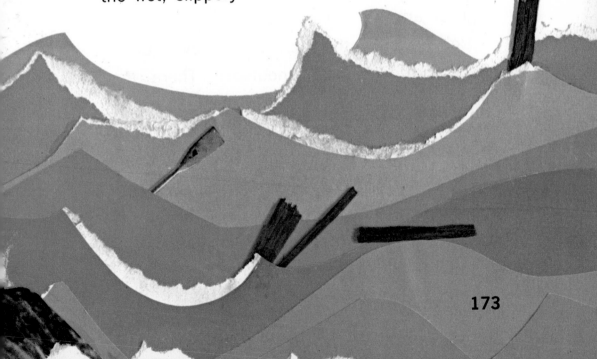

During the summer the Coast Guard patrols up and down the coast trying to spot people who are in trouble. Bob and Jim had just taken off when a call came in from the Sand Point Coast Guard Station.

"Sand Point to 'Copter 1400," the voice said. "A man reports seeing two boys stranded on Castle Rock. Check and report."

"Repeat," Bob answered.

The radio operator gave Bob careful directions to Castle Rock. Bob and Jim flew toward the rock. Jim tried to spot the boys. He put a pair of field glasses to his eyes.

"Take the 'copter lower," he said to Bob. "I see Castle Rock all right, but I still see no sign of anyone moving."

Bob lowered the big 'copter over Castle Rock. Suddenly Jim shouted. "There they are! I see two boys lying on the rock."

Bob flew as close to Castle Rock as he dared to go. Jim hurried to the back of the 'copter. He put on his safety belt.

"Hold her steady," he called to Bob. "I think we'd better take them up in the basket."

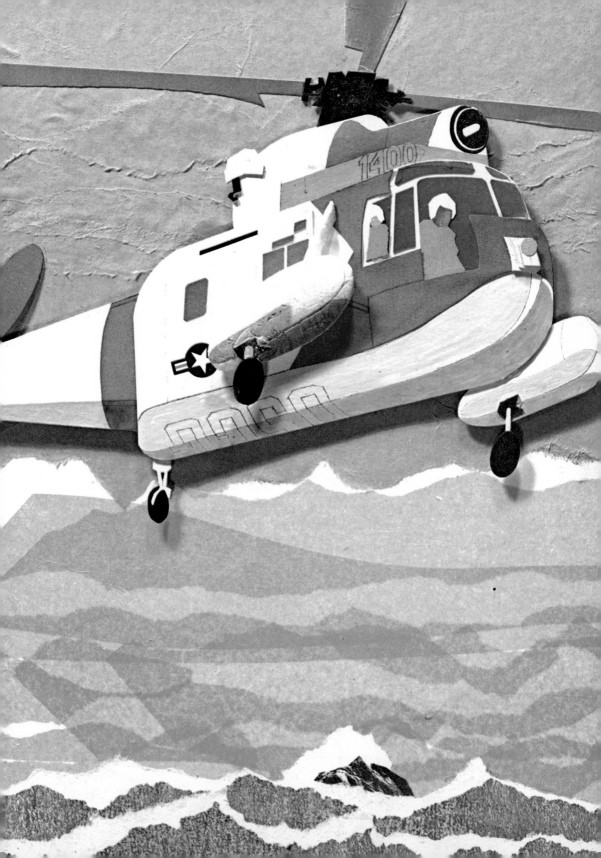

Jim hooked the basket to the hoist that hung from the roof inside the helicopter. Then he pressed the button that lowered the basket out of the hatch. When the basket hit the rock, Ron grabbed it and helped Pete climb into it. He was pulled up, dripping water and swinging in the wind. Jim hauled Pete into the 'copter and told him to lie on the cot. Then he lowered the basket for Ron.

Bob radioed the Station to tell them that they had found the boys and were going to have them checked at the hospital.

Jim covered the boys with warm blankets. "Take it easy," he said. "We'll be at the hospital in no time and have you looked over by a doctor. You had a close call, but you'll be all right."

The doctors were waiting for Ron and Pete. They checked them as soon as the boys came in. They dried their wet clothes and covered the boys with warm blankets. The Coast Guard called their parents to come after them.

Bob and Jim came to say good-by. "Thanks a lot," Ron said. "You saved our lives."

Pete opened one eye sleepily. "It was a great ride," he said. "Thanks."

Jim smiled. "Watch the tide next time, wherever you fish," he said. "And always let someone know where you're going and when you plan to be back. Then, if you're in trouble, people know where to look for you."

Bob and Jim took to the air again. "'Copter 1400 to Sand Point," Bob reported. "Rescue complete. The boys are in Sand Point Hospital. We are coming in now."

Bob and Jim started back to the Coast Guard Station. They were ready for dinner and a good night's sleep too. Tomorrow would be another day.

*Molly C. Gorelick*
and *Jean B. Graeber*

178

# MAN-MADE GIANTS

You could do everything that the machines in this story do—if you had plenty of friends to help you. People have always been able to work and to build wonderful things, using only their muscles. They can do a great deal more when they also use their brains. They can invent machines to make work thousands of times easier and faster.

The big machine in the picture is a shovel that's used for digging an enormous hole. In one bite, its scoop can tear out a chunk of earth more than twice as tall as a man. Its long arm, called the boom, lifts the load as high as the top of a seven-story building. Then the boom swings around and drops its load almost a city block away.

Shovels like this are made to work where beds of coal lie close to the surface of the earth, covered by a layer of soil. The shovel clears away the soil so that other machines can dig out the coal.

When a giant shovel has cleared off one spot, its crawlers begin to turn, and it creeps slowly ahead. But it can't travel on roads. It's far too big and heavy and tall—so big, in fact, that it came to the mine in pieces.

Forty-five freight cars were needed to haul all the parts for just one machine from the factory to the mine. Then experts put the parts together right where the shovel was to start digging.

And dig it does. In one minute its scoop can bite out as much dirt as 3,600 men could dig, using only their muscles to lift ordinary hand shovels !

The giant shovel is one of the biggest machines ever made, but there is another that can lift even bulkier things. It is an overhead crane that works in a shipyard.

Often the crane hoists big boilers out of ships so that repair men can work on them. It is so huge that it carries another crane on its back. The piggy-back crane—that's its real name—reaches down and lifts things off the deck of the ship too.

Hammering is another kind of muscle work that machines can do quickly and easily. Suppose the water pipes under your street need mending. Repair men have to tear up the pavement in order to reach the pipes. So they bring in jack hammers to do the pounding. Strong blasts of air run the hammers, and, in no time, the pavement is broken up.

Crushed rock was used for making the paved street in the first place. It came from a big machine called a rock crusher which breaks up chunks of stone into small pieces. Strong jaws inside the crusher chew at the stone until they have made it into bits that are just the right size.

An even bigger pounding machine is the pile driver. It can hammer a great thick log down into the ground almost as easily as a man can hammer a nail through a board.

One kind of pile driver does its pounding job with a steam piston. Another kind lifts a heavy weight and lets it bang down on top of the log, called a pile. The one in the picture works in a harbor. It drives piles deep into the earth that lies under water. A whole group of piles make the foundation for a pier in the harbor. Ships will be tied to the pier while their cargo is unloaded on it.

182

183

Harbors and rivers must be kept safe for ships. If mud and sand pile up in a thick layer on the bottom, ships may get stuck. So dredges go to work clearing the mud and sand away. Often a clean-up job takes a long time. The men who run the machinery live on the dredge, just as sailors live on a ship.

Some dredges have scoops that dig under water. Others, like the one in the picture, have suction pumps that work something like a giant vacuum cleaner. The mud or sand they suck up is called spoil.

Sometimes there is hard-caked mud under the water. Chopping machinery on the dredge breaks up the mud. Then it's ready to be pumped through a huge steel pipe that stretches away from the dredge like a great snake. The pipe pours the spoil out on land.

A dredge must stay in one place while it is working. So it carries along two huge spikes called spuds. These spuds move straight up and down at the stern of the dredge. When they ram down into the earth under water, they keep the dredge from drifting.

A spud is so heavy that it pokes its own hole in the muddy bottom of a river or harbor. But making holes on dry land is a different problem. For example, you can't just poke a telephone pole into the hard ground, or pound it in easily with a pile driver, either. So, in many places, a machine bores holes for telephone poles, just the way a carpenter bores a hole in wood with a brace and bit.

When the hole is ready the machine's long arms, reach out, lift a pole into the air, and plug it neatly down into place.

Long ago our ancestors discovered how to use simple tools—such as hammers, shovels, crowbars and rollers. These things seem very ordinary to us, but they were really wonderful inventions. The clever men who made them were providing ideas, one by one, which scientists and engineers used much later. Many of these old inventions have been made bigger, or combined with each other, in our great new machines.

*Mary Elting*

# MAN'S BEST FRIEND

Dogs have always had a very special place in people's lives. For almost as long as men have lived on the earth, dogs have lived with people, hunted and worked for them, and played with them.

All kinds and breeds of dogs love people and are loyal and faithful to their human friends. Some dogs are happiest playing with children. Some dogs are best for hunting, and some are better at work like bringing the cows home at night. There are dogs that like just to sit quietly beside a person, while others like to bounce and bark and play noisy games.

The Eskimo dog is a working dog that makes it possible for men to live in the great frozen North. There you might meet Nanook pulling a loaded sled over the ice and snow.

Many Eskimo dogs are tan or light-gray, but Nanook is snow-white. His heavy, bushy coat is so thick that he can sleep right in the snow even when the temperature is sixty or seventy degrees below zero. He has a double coat, and the undercoat is like warm winter underwear. Nanook is strong and lively and intelligent. He has great endurance, and can get along with very little to eat. This is important, because food is hard to find in the frozen North.

Nanook helps his master find food, for he can scent the breathing holes in deep ice where the fat seals come, and can lead his master there to spear them. Nanook can scent and round up musk ox and polar bears, and bring them to bay so that hunters can kill them. He helps haul home the fat and the meat and the skin with which a whole Eskimo village will be supplied.

Nanook can pull a small sled for a single hunter or traveler, but usually a team of dogs is hitched to a long sled, with a lead dog in front. The driver stands on the runners at the back of the sled and directs the team by cracking a long whip to the right or to the left. In summer, the dogs carry packs on their backs. They often bring mail and supplies to far-off lonely places.

Another of the working dogs is the German shepherd. One of the best jobs he does is to help blind people go around safely.

The guide dogs all go to school to learn how to work, and the masters must go too. They live together in the school while they learn to work together smoothly.

King is one of these shepherds who has been trained to be a guide dog. King is a big, thick-coated, strong shepherd with keen eyes and a good nose. He wears a harness specially designed for guide dogs, and his blind master holds the handgrip.

King guides his master across streets, up and down in elevators, into subways. He avoids dangerous places in the pavement, and low awnings that might hit the man's head.

One day King and his master were on their way to work when King stopped and would not let his master take another step.

"Go on, King! This is the main walk."

But King stood still. Then someone began to shout, "Watch out!" And King's master found out that part of the walk had caved in.

Guide dogs are allowed in trains and subways and classrooms. Masters are never without their watchful eyes.

193

Captain is a Doberman who lives in police barracks with the state troopers. Captain has a short, black, satiny coat. With his pointed nose, his slim, elegant body, and slender, long legs, he looks very dashing, but nobody would guess how terribly powerful he is.

Captain can run like the wind. He is not afraid of anything in the whole world. When he goes after a robber or criminal with Officer Foley, he can scale walls, jump through high windows, or run on the top of a narrow fence.

Dobermans make fine family dogs, too, and many people use them as watchdogs. Dobermans are happiest when they are doing something useful.

Another breed that helps the police is the bloodhound. A bloodhound named Benjamin lives in the barracks with Captain, and Officer Foley is proud of him too.

"The bloodhound is the best trailing dog in the world," he says, "and Benjamin is the best bloodhound I ever saw. He can find anyone."

Benjamin is a big, sad-looking dog with long, drooping ears and very deep-set, hazel eyes. His skin does not seem to fit him very well, and his forehead is always wrinkled as if he were worried about something. He is a shy, gentle, and noble dog, and visitors can go into his yard and pet him.

This is the way Benjamin works: When he is supposed to find someone, the officer lets him smell a glove or handkerchief or a piece of clothing belonging to that person. Then Benjamin puts his great, sad head down and begins to trail. He goes back and forth and up and down until his keen nose scents the place where the person who owned the object put down a foot. That is all Benjamin needs.

He begins to follow the trail and he goes through woods, over brooks, across streets, following the scent of that object until he finds the hunted person. The officer trails along behind Benjamin.

Benjamin once found a woman who had been lost in a swamp for two days. Officer Foley was very proud of him for the trail had become so faint or "cold" that only an intelligent dog like Benjamin could ever have smelled it at all!

*Gladys Taber*

# THE HAIRY DOG

My dog's so furry I've not seen
His face for years and years:
His eyes are buried out of sight
I only guess his ears.

When people ask me for his breed,
I do not know or care:
He has the beauty of them all
Hidden beneath his hair.

*Herbert Asquith*

**198**

# What Time Is It ?

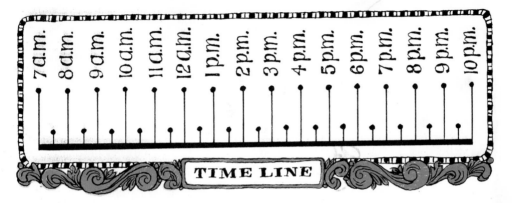

In this unit you have read about work and workers. You are also a worker. You have things you must do during the day. Make a large time line like the one above. Choose a day of the week and list next to each hour the things which you do at that time during the day. Begin with the hour you get up and end with the hour you go to bed. Be sure to include things you do just for fun.

Your list might include things you do:

at home          for your teacher

at school        for your mother

at the playground    for yourself

After you have completed your time line, choose a color and color in all the hours in which you work. With another color, color in all the hours in which you play.

**199**

# A New Alphabet

How well can you read a message written in a new alphabet?

Dear Jim,

ʋ^ʋ↗  πoobø

✓∩  ✓oo⊖⊖  Pʋoo⊖ʋ  Fʋ↗  δF↗ꭍ  oo～

～δ∩  bF↗๐oo๐๐⊖✶  ↗↗oo๐๐  ✓  ๓δFʋ^⊖✶

ʋF  ๐Fꭍ  ꭍ∩⊖⊖  ✓๐ʋↅF๐∩✶

## Key

The symbols of the new alphabet are in the same order as the letters of the alphabet you usually use.

| a | 𝒱 | e | ^ | i | ∞ | m | b | q | ♉ | u | ʋ | y | ♪ |
|---|---|---|---|---|---|---|---|---|---|---|---|---|---|
| b | r | f | ð | j | π | n | ～ | r | ↗ | v | σ | z | 8 |
| c | ↑ | g | ๐ | k | ꝙ | o | F | s | 𝓰 | w | γ | , | ø |
| d | ʋ | h | δ | l | ⊖ | p | ᴕ | t | ꭍ | x | ∝ | . | ✶ |

You might like to write a secret message to a friend in your classroom using the new alphabet.

# BEFORE You Were BORN

FRESH TEAS.

# MONEY OF LONG AGO

The Indians were living in America before the white man came. They traded things with each other as we do today. They used seashells for money and called it wampum.

The Indians used clam or conch shells to make the wampum. They ground the shells quite small, and rubbed them smooth and shiny. As they had only tools made of stone, making wampum was slow, hard work.

Wampum was made of light shells. It was also made of black and purple shells. The dark shells were much harder to find, and were of more value than the light shells. Two light shells equaled one dark wampum shell.

The Indians carried the wampum on a string. They bored a hole through each shell and strung the shells as we string beads. They wore the wampum as we wear jewelry.

Then people from faraway lands came to live in the New World. They settled in small colonies and were called colonists. They needed to build homes, and they needed food and clothing.

Since the Indians had corn and furs and meat, the colonists traded with the Indians. Because the Indians used wampum for money, the colonists began to use it too. They also traded pots and other household articles for things the Indians had.

# TOBACCO

The colonists saw the Indians raising a plant that looked like a long-leafed weed. They saw them smoke and chew this weed, which we know as tobacco. Of course the colonists had to try it. They began to raise tobacco for their own use.

After tobacco became popular in the colonies, the colonists began to ship some of the crop to England. It was considered so valuable that people began using tobacco for money. The Indians and the colonists were now using wampum and tobacco for money.

The colonists who came from England were fond of tea. They were used to drinking tea and missed not having it in America.

Since tea had to be brought by slow sailing ships to the colonies, it was very expensive.

The people who had tea began to use it for trading. Now the colonists were using three kinds of money—wampum, tobacco, and tea.

The people in America needed nails to help build their homes and churches. The English government had passed a law which said that no English colony could make its own nails. This law forced the people to buy their nails from England. The nails became so valuable that they were used for money, also. Have you ever heard of a ten-penny nail, or a twenty-penny nail? One hundred nails were worth ten pennies. One hundred larger nails equaled twenty pennies.

# MUSKET BALLS

The people who came to America to form colonies brought their guns. These guns were called muskets and were very heavy. They shot balls made of lead.

But lead was not easy to get, and it had to be melted before it could be molded into bullets. Before long the colonists began to use musket balls in the place of money.

The Indians and the colonists used wampum, tobacco, tea, nails, and musket balls for money for many years. They also used bags of salt, animal skins, and other things for trading.

*Elizabeth A. Campbell*

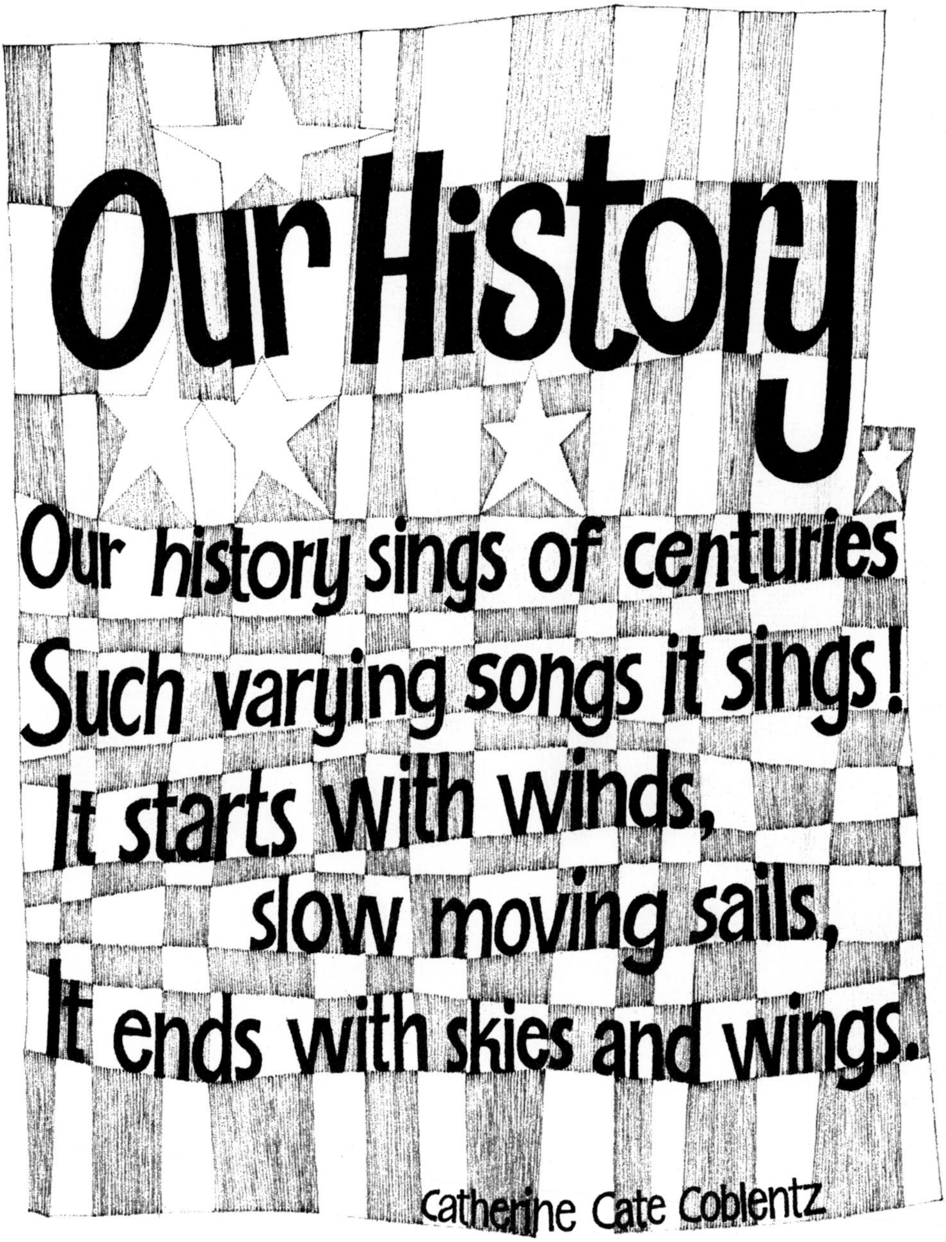

# Our History

Our history sings of centuries
Such varying songs it sings!
It starts with winds,
        slow moving sails,
It ends with skies and wings.

Catherine Cate Coblentz

# A Remarkable Man

In the year 1732 when George Washington was born, a little baby three months old was living on a farm in Maryland not far away. His name was Benjamin Banneker. He and George Washington grew up at the same time. Today, more than two hundred years later, we have reason to remember both men with pride.

Benjamin's grandparents worked hard on their farm in a Maryland valley. When Ben was six years old, his father was able to buy land next to Grandmother's farm. Here Ben lived all his long life.

Ben was twelve years old when a man named Peter Heinrich moved into the valley. Soon Peter Heinrich's brother would bring his family to live there too. Who would teach his brother's children? The nearest school was far away.

Mr. Heinrich talked to the other families in the valley. Yes, they would give money to start a school and Peter Heinrich would be the teacher. "My school will be for the sons of *all* free men," he announced.

And so it was that Ben went to a school for the first time of his life. His grandmother had taught him to read, but going to school was even more wonderful. Ben learned quickly, for he was eager to know about many things. He was especially good in mathematics. Peter Heinrich took great interest in Ben and lent him books to read at home.

Some years later, when Ben was a young man, he met a traveler from Europe who had come to Maryland on business. The man had a gold watch, the first that Ben had seen. How did it work? The man opened the case and showed Ben the tiny parts inside. "Keep it until I come again," he said.

Peter Heinrich lent Ben more books and gave him a picture of a big clock torn from an English paper. Ben studied these, but still he was not sure how the clock worked.

One night he decided that he would have to take the watch apart. By the light of a wick floating in a plate of oil, he carefully took out each part. He made a drawing as he worked so that he could put the watch together again.

Ben decided to build a clock that would strike the hours. He worked for more than two years, cutting and shaping each piece out of wood. At last he had a clock that kept time and struck the hours. People came from far and near to see it. Ben's clock was the first of its kind made in America.

In 1772 the Ellicott family moved into the valley. The Ellicotts became good friends of Ben's. They soon learned how interested he was in everything. They gave him a telescope and books on astronomy. Ben spent many nights lying on his back watching the stars through his telescope. He studied the books. Soon he became famous as an astronomer as well as a clockmaker.

In 1789, General George Washington became the first President of the new country, the United States of America. But the country had no capital. Many cities wanted that honor. Finally it was decided to build a brand new city. President Washington was asked to select a place for the new city. He chose a spot on the Potomac River, between the states of Maryland and Virginia.

One day George Ellicott came with news of an important job for Ben. "Would you like to help lay out and build the new capital—the capital of the United States?" he asked Ben.

Ben was overcome. "Help build the capital of our country? Of course I would!"

President Washington named Major Pierre L'Enfant, a French engineer, to design the city. Benjamin Banneker and George Ellicott would be surveyors working with him.

Most of the land was wild, with a few farms here and there. Major L'Enfant chose a hill for the Capitol building. He planned wide streets and open spaces. The city was to be truly beautiful. Ben and the surveyors measured the land and ran lines for the streets. The work went on for months.

In time there was trouble. Major L'Enfant left, taking the plans for the city with him. Thomas Jefferson, who was Secretary of State, called a meeting to see what could be done. Everyone was unhappy. "It would seem that the job must be done all over again," Mr. Jefferson said. "Does anyone have any ideas?"

Benjamin Banneker rose to his feet. "I have the plans in my head," he said. "I would be happy to draw them up."

"How long would it take?"

"Two or three days, sir," was the reply.

People had often spoken of Benjamin Banneker's remarkable memory. But this was almost unheard of ! Three days to draw plans that had taken months to prepare !

Benjamin Banneker knew what he could do. Three days later he delivered the plans to Mr. Jefferson. The work went on. And today our capital city is indeed one of the most beautiful cities in the world. It was named for our first President. And it was built from the plan that Benjamin Banneker had carried in his head.

*Gretchen Wulfing*

Benjamin Banneker
(1731-1806)

astronomer    publisher    surveyor

inventor    mathematician    engineer

# BARNUM'S FIRST CIRCUS

"Phineas," said his father, pushing back his coffee cup, "you can tend store for me the next two or three days. The mare's going to take your mother and me to town." He looked across the table at his thirteen-year-old son.

Phineas Barnum stopped munching a doughnut and his eyes lighted up. This piece of news was too good to be true. He had often helped his father in the store. But to have it in charge—that would be wonderful!

"Yes, sir," he answered.

His father went on, "Don't give the Widow Sweeney any credit. Cash in hand is the rule. Seeing apples are good this year, you can take two or three barrels in pay for groceries. But, remember, you're to tend to your job and not talk your head off. You've got a good head on your shoulders when you want to use it. That's all. And don't make me use that strap hanging up in the barn when I come back Saturday." His eyes twinkled.

Phineas put on his hat and made his way to his father's corner store.

He started a fire in the rusty iron stove in the center of the store. The fire had not been going fifteen minutes before the Widow Sweeney came in. She slammed the store door so that everything on the shelves rattled.

"Well, so it's Barnum's boy!" she said. The son should be much easier to deal with than the father. "Now I'd like you to tie up a pound of tea and two pounds of coffee and a pound of rice."

Young Barnum went to the shelves and began putting up her order. At last everything was ready. In his pleasantest tone, he said, "One dollar, if you please, Mrs. Sweeney."

The widow started back. "No sass from you, Phineas Barnum. This is on credit today. I'm a poor woman and I pay up my bills all at once, twice a year."

"Pa said no credit—that I'd have to take cash only," answered Phineas. "I'm sorry, but you owe a lot already, Mrs. Sweeney."

The widow began again. "Now you're a good boy. Haven't I got the nicest little calf only two weeks old that I was planning on giving your pa to pay my bill?"

"Is it an all-right calf?" asked Phineas.

"Of course it's all right! It's as pretty as can be. But there's one strange thing about it—an extra eye."

"Oh!" Joy gleamed in Phineas' own eyes. If he could only get hold of that calf for his own use!

"Well, marm—" he began. "If you'll let me stop around tonight and see it when I close up store, I'd let you have these things now."

The widow agreed, warmed herself at the stove, and then went on her way.

Phineas Barnum made up his mind to show off that three-eyed calf behind his father's barn for a penny a peep—or maybe he'd charge two cents. What a find for the show he was planning!

Next came a red-headed boy, younger than himself, who lugged in two pecks of apples to be traded for potatoes. As he set the basket down with a thump, a snake glided across the floor toward the heat of the stove.

"Hi, help me get him, Phin! He must have got out of my pocket!" cried Hiram. Young Barnum caught the snake, and shut him up in a small dark box.

"Can you do tricks with him?" asked Phineas.

"Only caught him yesterday," said Hiram.

"Bring him around to my house Saturday afternoon. Meet me behind the barn. We'll have a circus," said Phineas. "There's lots of things I'd tell you but I've got to tend store now."

Hiram chuckled. "I'll see you later and I'll get George and Buck too."

Three farmers opened the door and came in. "Hey, Phineas," said the first farmer, Ezra Dean, "give me two pounds of ten-penny nails."

The busy storekeeper weighed them and was paid. "Two pennies more," he said.

Ezra dumped his purse out on the counter. Not a cent was in it.

"I'll give you a hopping bean instead, boy," he said. "Know you like tricks."

"Does it really hop? Let me see for sure."

Ezra winked at the other men and pulled a small brown bean from his pocket. Placing it on the bottom of a broken cracker box, he carried it to the iron stove. Sure enough, the heat caused it to skip about here and there on the piece of board.

"I haven't seen anything like that in a month of Sundays," said Mose Painter, the eldest of the three.

Phineas put the hopping bean carefully into his pocket. "Thank you kindly," he said.

As he waited on children and housewives, Phineas could hear the farmers talking.

"Just try walking easy by that mill at twilight, and you'll hear a high, queer voice like a spirit's," one man said.

"Is that so? I didn't know it was haunted."

"Well, 'tis. Steve Carter lost his watch chain going by there, a week or so ago."

"Time someone got to the bottom of this," said Mose Painter.

The very same evening, Phineas went to see Widow Sweeney's three-eyed calf and agreed to take it. On the way home he walked past the old mill. He did not believe what the men at the store had said about its being haunted. In the moonlight the stone mill looked as peaceful as the stream that flowed beside it.

Suddenly, from an upper window of the place came a voice. "Good boy," it said, then a shadow flew past him. Something jingled at his feet. Phineas drew from his pocket a bit of bread. The shadow drew nearer and perched on his finger. It was a raven!

"Good night," it croaked. "Have no fear, no fear."

Phineas caught the bird and slipped it into a bag he had brought. Then he picked up the thing on the ground. It was nothing less than Steve Carter's gold watch chain! What a surprise that would be for Steve on Saturday!

A raven would be great for the side shows. He'd teach it to talk in no time. There was never going to be another circus like this one he planned. No, *sir* !

Next morning Phineas had Hiram and his brother George take a turn about the town. In their hands they carried a pile of hand-printed notices that they stuck under front doors or handed to anyone they met.

Saturday came at last. His father was still away, but at three o'clock Phineas had planned to close up the store until evening. His friends were already at work preparing the circus behind the barn. "Barnum's Saturday Show" was opening at three o'clock. Phineas had decided to charge a nickel, and a penny more for side shows.

"This way, Ladies and Gentlemen," he shouted, "to see the Three-Eyed Calf, the only one of its kind. Meet the snake that snuggles up to you like a baby. See the Magic Bean, and Lupo, the raven that talks and brings forth gold. Last chance, cash and tickets!"

Farmers were driving up in carts and buggies with their children. Big boys were coming in, leading their younger brothers and sisters.

"This way, this way to the calf. Put your money on the Three-Eyed-Calf!" called Barnum.

When the crowd had seen all the side shows, Phineas brought out the raven.

"Step up here," he said. "Plenty of room to stand. Step up!" Then, "What do you like best, Lupo?" he asked, holding up the raven.

"Gold," said Lupo in a deep voice.

"What next to that?"

"Chain," croaked the raven.

"And then?"

"Gold chain."

"Now, tell the gentleman that you are sorry you took his watch chain."

"Sorry," said Lupo.

Steve Carter, his eyes popping, was called up to claim his missing watch chain.

"Well, I vow," was all he could say.

Doughnuts and cider were being passed to the crowd when a horse was heard down the road. Soon the tired mare appeared on the far side of the barn. In the buggy was Pa Barnum with his wife by his side.

"PHINEAS!" he called in tones to wake the dead, "you come here and stop this fooling." He stopped the buggy, got out and rushed over to the circus.

"Nickel, please, Mr. Barnum," said the boy who now was gatekeeper. Barnum paid it and went in to look for Phineas.

Suddenly, in a nearby pen, he saw a fine little calf. It was sound in every way except for a third eye on the left side.

Then father and son met, face to face.

"Hello, Pa," Phineas said. "See the calf you got from the Widow Sweeney."

"How much did you give for it?" roared his father.

"Not a penny. It was a present on payment."

"Well! And what have you got to say about closing up the store and losing my Saturday afternoon trade?"

"I was going to re-open this evening," said his son, "and what I've taken in at the circus will make up for any loss. I've got a good sight of money in here, Pa, and it's yours!" He rattled a tin can by his father's ear.

"You've not cheated anybody to get hold of these critters?"

"No, Pa, I didn't cheat. When folks come to a circus, I like to show them a thing or two," Phineas said. "And I only quit the store an hour ago."

His father scratched his head. "I always took it you had smartness in you," he said.

The younger Barnum looked happily around. The crowd was beginning to scatter. His father had quieted down and was peering into this box and that pen to see what else he could see. But somehow the barn lot was not large enough for Phineas. Some day there must be a white tent or maybe a hall. And some day, yes, some day—he'd have it, too!

*Laura Benét*

233

# OUR

We had a circus in our shed
(Admission, three new pins a head)
And every girl and boy I know
Is talking yet about our show.

They laughed so hard at Fatty Brown
When he came out to be the clown,
That all the neighbors ran to see
Whatever such a noise could be.

Our tin-pan and mouth-organ band
Played tunes that sounded simply grand;
We had a truly sawdust ring,
Pink lemonade, 'n everything.

The big menagerie was nice:
Three cats, one dog, and five white mice,
A parrot that Bill's uncle lent;
All underneath a bedspread tent.

Then Ned and Buster took a sheet
That covered them from head to feet
And made a horse that kicked and pranced
And when it heard the band, it danced.

And Sally Ann was "Bareback Queen"!
No finer rider could be seen;
She stood right up, and looked so proud,
But kissed her hand to all the crowd.

We took some chalk—blue, green, and red—
And made a "Tattooed Man" of Fred;
Jim juggled lighted cigarettes,
And Tom turned double somersets.

We had tall stilts—and flying rings—
And lots and lots of other things—
And every boy and girl I know
Said yes, it was a *dandy* show!

*Laura Lee Randall*

# Grandpa and the Tin Lizzie

Grandpa's mind was made up. He was going to buy an automobile! Yes, Grandpa said, times were changing. Horse and buggy days were at an end. He wanted to keep up with the times and so he was going to buy a Ford, a model-T Ford.

Emily was on pins and needles for fear Grandpa might change his mind about keeping up with the times, but at last the great day came.

It was Emily who went out to sit on the front steps and saw Grandpa driving down the road as nice as you please. "He's coming!" she shouted. "He's coming!"

There he came, down the road and across the bridge and up Main Street. Beaming and proud, he drew up in front of the house. "Whoa!" he cried as he stopped his new automobile.

Because Emily was related to the car, she felt free to climb into the front seat and bounce up and down on the leather cushions.

"Come along, Emily," said Mama.

"But I want to go for a ride," cried Emily.

"Now, Emily," said Mama firmly. "You are not to set foot in that automobile for a good long time. I just don't trust your grandfather's driving."

"Mama!" wailed Emily.

As the days went by, Emily's mother made up excuses to keep Emily out of her grandfather's automobile, and Emily watched wistfully as he rattled around town, keeping up with the times.

Then one Sunday Grandpa and Grandma drove over to Emily's house in the new Ford. "Come on," said Grandpa. "We've come to take the whole family for a ride."

"Good," said Daddy. "I've been itching to go for a ride."

This time there was no way out for Mama. Emily and her mother and father climbed into the back seat. Grandpa got out and cranked the car—and cranked it and cranked it. Finally the engine started, with a noise like machinery sneezing, and the automobile began to shake. Grandpa ran around and climbed in fast and off they drove.

What a ride they had! Down Main Street, past the school, down an unpaved road trailing dust and scattering chickens, up Main Street, back home. And they had not hit a cow or even a chicken!

"Say, Emily," said Grandpa, before he and Grandma drove off, "how would you like to drive out to the old Skinner place with me in the morning?" The old Skinner place was a piece of land which Grandpa owned and which was farmed for him by a nearby farmer.

"Oh, Grandpa, I would love to," answered Emily quickly.

The next morning bright and early, Grandpa came for Emily. It was a beautiful day for a drive in the country in an automobile with the top down.

The road was good and bumpy, and Emily enjoyed every bump they hit. "Can you go faster, Grandpa?" she asked. Grandpa pulled down the gas lever on the steering wheel. The Ford leaped ahead. Emily jounced and bounced around on the leather seat. "Grandpa!" Emily shrieked, "We're going twenty-five miles an hour!" The joy of it! Tearing along at twenty-five miles an hour!

Farther out in the country the wagon road wound through several farms and at each farm Grandpa had to stop.

He climbed out over the door, opened the gate, climbed back into his Ford, drove through, got out and closed the gate, climbed back in, and drove on to the next gate. The first section of the road led them through a barnyard, where Grandpa had to swerve to avoid some chickens and a calf.

Finally they reached the old Skinner place. How quiet it was with the engine of Grandpa's car turned off! Grandpa climbed out to examine his alfalfa crop while Emily picked some wild flowers growing along the fence to take home to Mama.

"Come on, Emily," Grandpa called at last. "Time to go."

Emily and her grandfather were not even near the first gate when Grandpa began to work the clutch pedal up and down. It seemed lifeless under his foot.

"Grandpa!" Emily was alarmed.

"Great Scott!" Grandpa was alarmed too. "Now what the Sam Hill was it the salesman said to do in a case like this?" He pumped the clutch once more before it came to him. "He said if this ever happened I'd better not stop, because I couldn't get the engine started again unless I was on a hill."

"Then don't stop!" shouted Emily. The gate seemed to be flying toward her. "Grandpa, don't stop!"

"I've got to!" yelled Grandpa.

"No!" shrieked Emily. "Then we'll never get home!"

Just when Emily thought they were going to crash into the gate, Grandpa turned aside and his automobile went bounding around in his alfalfa crop. Grandpa drove around and around in a circle. "It's no use, Emily," he said. "I'll have to stop. There's nothing else to do. We can hike to the nearest farm and get a farmer with a team to tow us back to town."

"No, wait, Grandpa," begged Emily. Be towed back to town behind old-fashioned horses? I should say not! Grandpa and his wonderful new automobile would be the laughing stock of the whole town. "If you drive real slow," she suggested, "I could jump out and open the gate."

"Emily, you'll get hurt," Grandpa said.

"No, I'll be careful," Emily answered.

"I guess I could see how slow I could drive." Grandpa was not eager to be towed back by horses. They slowed down until they were bouncing gently over the ruts.

Emily laid her bunch of flowers on the seat. She opened the door and looked down. The ground was passing by faster than she had expected. She took a deep breath and jumped. She stumbled and skinned her knee. "I'm all right," she called out as she ran to the gate, climbed up and unlatched the gate. She pushed off with one foot and, riding the gate, she swung across the road.

Grandpa drove through the gate and started going around in circles in the next field. Emily hopped off the gate before the dust had settled and pushed and shoved until it was closed once more. She slipped the circle of wire back in place and ran after the Ford. She had worked fast, because this field of wheat did not belong to Grandpa and the farmer who owned it might not like Grandpa driving around on his crop.

Grandpa slowed down until Emily was afraid the engine would stop. She grabbed the edge of the Ford beside the seat cushion and pulled herself up on the running board. Then she flopped into the seat. Whew! She had made it!

"Good work, Emily," said Grandpa, and drove in a straight line down the wagon road once more.

Emily leaned back to catch her breath before the next gate. If she had done it once, she could do it again. She had to or be towed back by horses.

At the second gate Grandpa began to circle once more. Emily opened the door and leaped bravely through the air. She stumbled again but managed not to fall. She must be getting the hang of it. Once more she slipped off the wire hoop. This gate creaked and Emily could not ride it. She had to shove. Grandpa straightened out his driving and went through. Emily tried not to breathe dust while she struggled to close the gate, and Grandpa circled through the oats until she could scramble aboard. Whew! That was hard work! Emily hoped she had enough strength left for the third and last gate.

That gate was in sight of some farm buildings. Grandpa circled slowly. Emily took a deep breath and leaped. Yes, she did seem to have the hang of it, because she landed on her feet. She ran to the gate, unlatched it, and tried to open it. It would not budge. Frantically Emily shoved. What if Grandpa ran out of gas while he was circling around!

"Don't stop, Grandpa," she begged. "I'll think of something."

A calf came bounding across the barnyard to see what was going on. It would be dreadful if he got through the gate. Emily would never be able to catch him in that big field and Grandpa really would run out of gas while she tried. The calf frolicked over and nuzzled her with his moist nose. "Shoo!" she cried. "Go away!"

The farmer came out of the barn with a pitchfork in his hands. "What the Sam Hill is going on here?" he yelled, dropping the pitchfork and running toward Emily.

"Don't stop, Grandpa," pleaded Emily.

"What are you driving around in my oats for?" demanded the farmer.

"I can't stop," yelled Grandpa. "I'll never get her started again."

"Please open the gate," begged Emily.

The farmer began to laugh. Then he opened the gate for Emily.

"Oh, thank you," said Emily, with great feeling. "Thank you ever so much."

The farmer stood watching Emily with something like admiration as she leaped to the running board when Grandpa drove by.

"Thank you, sir," Grandpa yelled above the noise of the engine.

"You're welcome," the farmer yelled back. "Next time get a horse!"

"Yes, sir, Emily," said Grandpa, as they headed back toward town, "I always said you were a humdinger."

The ride back to town was peaceful enough. When they came to Main Street, Grandpa said, "You know, I have a feeling your mother might not think too highly of what went on this morning. Maybe we'd better keep it a secret, you and me."

"Yes, let's," agreed Emily, who was happy Grandpa wasn't going to tell, either. Secrets were fun and she was pleased that she and Grandpa had one all their own to share.

"Whoa!" cried Grandpa, stopping in front of the house just as if there was nothing wrong with his model-T.

When Emily climbed out, she found that her legs felt wobbly. "Thank you for the ride, Grandpa," she said, not feeling the least bit like a humdinger.

Grandpa's eyes twinkled. "Thank *you*, Emily. I don't know how I'd have managed without you."

Emily walked into the house on shaky legs. "Did you have a nice ride, Emily?" asked Mama.

"Yes, Mama." Wearily Emily sat down to rest.

"Emily, I have been thinking. Your grandfather is right. Times are changing and he is right to keep up with them, even at his age."

As Emily bent over to examine her skinned knee, she could not help thinking that it had been all she could do to keep up with Grandpa's tin Lizzie.

*Beverly Cleary*

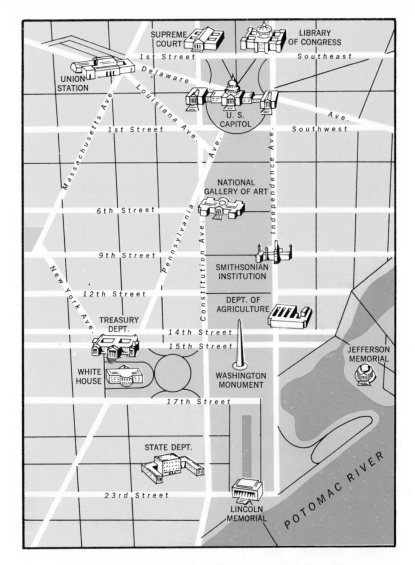

# Where in Washington, D.C.?

If you went to Washington D.C. by train, arriving at Union Station, what streets would you follow to see all the places pictured on the map? Try to go to each place only once.

# Could It Be ?

Here's Mr. Barnum in his office. How many mistakes can you find in this picture and how do you know that they are mistakes ?

MAGIC
OF
OLD

6

# KAPOÏ and the OWL KING

Many years ago, my little brothers and sisters, in the old, old days, there lived in the Rainbow Valley in the island of Hawaii, a man named Kapoï.* He was very poor and had to work from dawn to dusk for food to keep his bones from showing. His grass-house was decaying and its roof was falling to pieces, so that it was little more than a shelter from the worst of the rain.

*Kä pō ē

254

One afternoon he went to the nearby marsh to cut a bundle of grass to mend the thatch, when to his joy he came upon an owl's nest with seven eggs in it.

Saying to himself, "This is my good luck, and I shall have a feast this night," he carried the eggs carefully home, and having washed them and wrapped them in cabbage-tree leaves, he built a fire in the earth in front of the house, and heated the stones red hot to bake them. But as he was about to lay them on the hot stones, there came from a tree whose branches overhung his doorway the *tu-whoo* of an owl, and a voice said, "O Kapoï, give me back my eggs!"

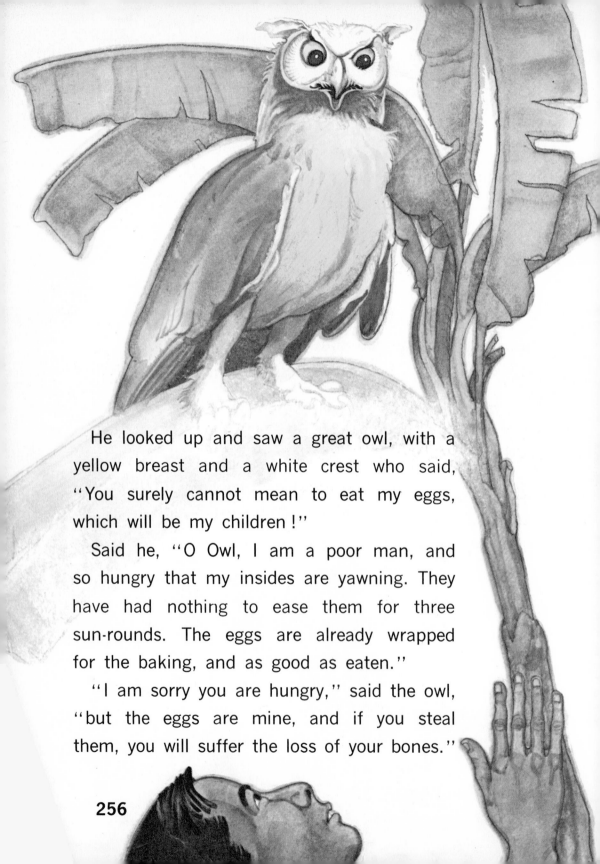

He looked up and saw a great owl, with a yellow breast and a white crest who said, "You surely cannot mean to eat my eggs, which will be my children!"

Said he, "O Owl, I am a poor man, and so hungry that my insides are yawning. They have had nothing to ease them for three sun-rounds. The eggs are already wrapped for the baking, and as good as eaten."

"I am sorry you are hungry," said the owl, "but the eggs are mine, and if you steal them, you will suffer the loss of your bones."

256

"Well," said Kapoï, "I am not completely
without kindness, and you will have them."
And he set the eggs in the grass, and the
owl flew down, and one by one carried them
off in its beak to its nest.

When it came for the last one, it said, "O
Kapoï, you shall not suffer for your kindness.
There are things worse than hunger, and in
a tight spot, even an owl may help you. If
you would make me and my tribe your
friends, build a temple of apple wood for us
in the forest, and once each moon lay on its
altar three bananas." Having said this, it
cried its *tu-whoo* three times, and flew away
with the seventh egg.

From that day Kapoï's luck changed for the better. His garden grew well, and hunger visited him no more. And soon he built in the forest the little temple, on whose altar he laid each moon the three bananas.

Now the King of the land, unknown to Kapoï, had begun to build a great temple to his gods, and he had ordered that no man should build another until it was finished. Someone told him what Kapoï had done. The King was angry and sent armed men who dragged Kapoï before him. Poor Kapoï was ordered killed and baked in the King's oven as a sacrifice for the big temple.

On the third evening after that, as Kapoï lay alone, guarded by the priests, he heard a low *tu-whoo*, and the great owl with the white crest and yellow breast flew in the doorway. Said he, "O Kapoï, fear not. I am the King of the owls, and it was my seven eggs you gave back when you were hungry."

"Alas!" moaned Kapoï. "I am in a place where none can help me. For tomorrow's sunrise will see me killed on the King's altar!"

"Oh, no!" said the owl. "Do you think owls are so helpless? Three days ago, when word was brought me that the King had ordered you killed, I sent messengers to all the islands and to every forest of all this Hawaii. Now twenty thousand owls have come to rescue you. Listen and you will hear them."

So saying, it flew to the doorway, and flapped its wings three times. Throughout all the grove about the temple there arose a flapping of wings, like the sound of a great wind. Then, bidding him be of good cheer, the owl flew away.

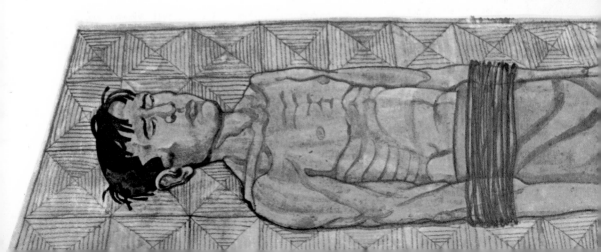

All through the night, as the priests gathered, while the torches flared and the drums beat, Kapoï waited. At dawn the priests in their red cloaks came in where he lay, chanting their prayer-songs, and the men with big clubs, and hope died in his breast.

But even as they waited for the signal to kill him, there rose a sound outside like the howl of a hurricane, and in through the doorway came flying a screeching army of owls. In thousands, with knifelike beaks stabbing, and hooked claws tearing, they swooped down upon the priests. Their beating wings drowned the drums, and their screams pierced the heavens.

The King's men fought them, till they were blinded. They fled from the temple, seeing the whole sky clouded with the great birds. Then the owls with their sharp beaks set Kapoï free, and he went home, wondering.

When the news came to the King, he was frightened. He ordered that his new temple should be dedicated to the Owl King, and that the owls of the Rainbow Valley should be protectors of the King, and they are counted so to this day.

As for Kapoï, the King made him a High-Chief, and he named him one of his Counselors, and his son and his son's son after him.

*Hawaiian Tale*
Adapted by *Post Wheeler*

# FABLE

The mountain and the squirrel
Had a quarrel,
And the former called the latter "Little Prig";
Bun replied,
"You are doubtless very big;
But all sorts of things and weather
Must be taken in together,
To make up a year
And a sphere.
And I think it no disgrace
To occupy my place.
If I'm not so large as you,
You are not so small as I,
And not half so spry.
I'll not deny you make
A very pretty squirrel track;
Talents differ; all is well and wisely put;
If I cannot carry forests on my back,
Neither can you crack a nut."

*Ralph Waldo Emerson*

# THE WORLD'S SMARTEST CAT

Mrs. Burger kept chickens. She kept geese. She kept pigs.

Mr. Burger used to come in to supper and find her busy chasing pigs back into the pen, chasing chickens out of her garden, and geese off the porch. "Sure got enough animals here to keep you busy," he'd say.

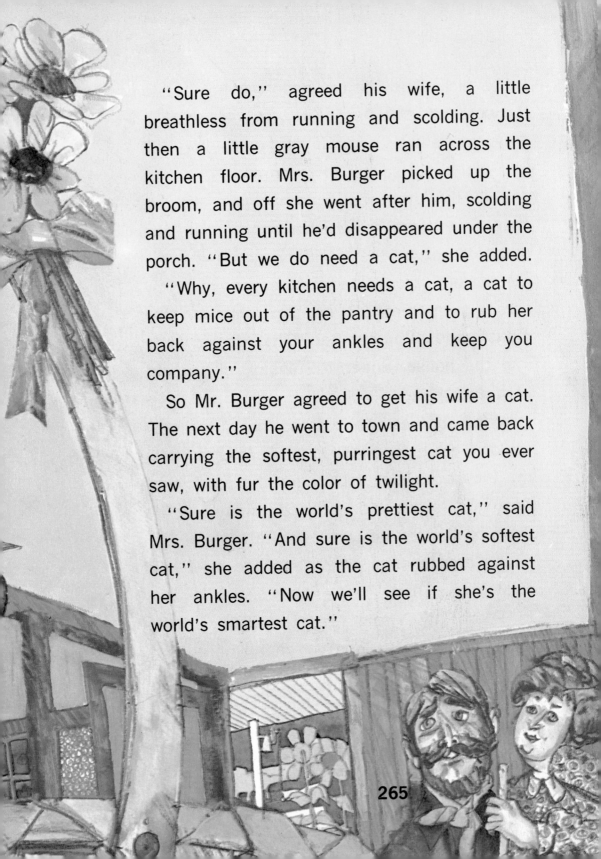

"Sure do," agreed his wife, a little breathless from running and scolding. Just then a little gray mouse ran across the kitchen floor. Mrs. Burger picked up the broom, and off she went after him, scolding and running until he'd disappeared under the porch. "But we do need a cat," she added.

"Why, every kitchen needs a cat, a cat to keep mice out of the pantry and to rub her back against your ankles and keep you company."

So Mr. Burger agreed to get his wife a cat. The next day he went to town and came back carrying the softest, purringest cat you ever saw, with fur the color of twilight.

"Sure is the world's prettiest cat," said Mrs. Burger. "And sure is the world's softest cat," she added as the cat rubbed against her ankles. "Now we'll see if she's the world's smartest cat."

She picked up the cat and took her out to the porch. "Look here, Kitty. Here's where a gray mouse lives, and if you catch him, I'll give you a big saucer of cream."

Well, the gray mouse soon gave Kitty a chance to prove whether she was the smartest cat in the world or not. He came racing out from under the porch. Kitty sprang after him. Up on the porch ran the mouse, and after him ran Kitty. He led Kitty into the house, under the chairs, all around here and there.

Poor Kitty raced and chased, but she simply couldn't catch that gray mouse. After a while the mouse disappeared under the porch and was safe in his hiding place. Kitty just lay down on the ground and looked after him. She hadn't even enough strength left to mew and scratch after him.

"Poor Kitty," said Mrs. Burger. "All that racing and chasing, and you didn't quite earn your saucer of cream." But Mrs. Burger knew what hard work chasing is, so she poured Kitty a big saucer of cream anyway.

The next day the gray mouse came out of his hiding place just long enough to give Kitty another wild run. Then he disappeared under the porch again, and Kitty was left worn out.

"Poor Kitty," said Mrs. Burger, again feeling sorry for the cat and again giving her a big saucer of cream.

Now Kitty did turn into the world's nicest house cat, rubbing her soft back against Mrs. Burger's ankles and being just the best sort of purring company. But there was one thing Kitty never could do and that was to catch the gray mouse.

The mouse just got fatter—and faster. Every couple of days he'd turn up and make Kitty chase him all over without letting her get anywhere near enough to catch him. And, of course, even though Kitty didn't catch the mouse, Mrs. Burger felt sorry for her and kept giving her saucers of cream.

One day Mr. Burger came in from the fields and saw Mrs. Burger poking under the porch with a broom handle.

"What's gotten under there now? A pig?"

"Nope," said Mrs. Burger, poking away like fury.

"Must be your silly chickens, then."

"Nope. It's not pigs or chickens. It's that gray mouse I'm after. Just keeps gettin' fatter and faster, faster and fatter. Near tuckered poor Kitty out again, making her chase him and then just skipping out of sight."

269

Mrs. Burger kept on grumbling and searching around with the broom handle, and Mr. Burger tiptoed into the kitchen to see whether poor tired-out Kitty was perking up by now. There was Kitty in the middle of the kitchen floor, lapping cream out of a big saucer. And there, right beside her, was that gray mouse sharing her treat.

American Folk Tale
Ellen Margolis

# I Wouldn't

There's a mouse house
In the hall wall
With a small door
By the hall floor
Where the fat cat
Sits all day,
Sits that way
All day
Every day
Just to say,
"Come out and play"
To the nice mice
In the mouse house
In the hall wall
With the small door
By the hall floor.

And do they
Come out and play
When the fat cat
Asks them to?

Well, would you?

John Ciardi

# How Beaver Got His Fine Fur

In the days when the earth was new and there were no men but only the animals, the sun was far away in the sky. It was so far away that there was no summer. It was so far away that the trees and the grasses and the flowers did not grow as they should. It was so far away that the acorns never set upon the oaks, and the blossoms never came on the clover, and the corn did not tassel so that there were no ears to ripen. It was so far away that the water in the rivers was always cold, and the fish stayed on the bottom of the streams and the tadpoles never became frogs.

272

He-Who-Made-the-Animals saw how it was, that there was not enough sun to heat the earth, so he made a snare. When the sun was away, and there was darkness, he set a pole in the path of the sun, and fastened a leather thong to it and laid a loop of the thong upon the sun's path. The sun did not see the snare in his path. The sun walked into the snare, and the snare held him fast.

Then the sun was close to the earth. The heat of the sun set the acorns and brought the clover into blossom and tasseled the corn and the ears of corn filled. The heat of the sun warmed the rivers so that the fish came up from the bottom and the tadpoles became frogs. Summer came to the earth. Hot summer came to the earth, and there was no night. There was only day, with the sun shining hot upon the earth.

273

Day after day the sun shone and the earth dried and the leaves on the trees withered, and the grasses turned brown and died and the corn died, and there was not enough water left in the rivers for the fish.

The animals called a council. The animals spoke to the sun.

"Sun," the animals said, "you give too much heat to the earth."

"Set me free from this snare," the sun said, "and I will go away."

"But if you go away, then there will not be enough heat. The earth will be as it was before He-Who-Made-the-Animals set the snare in your path," the animals said.

"Set me free," the sun said, "and I will come to the edge of the earth in the morning and in the evening. Set me free, and at noon-time I will stand straight above the earth and warm it so that the trees and the grasses and the flowers will grow and there will be many fish in the streams."

"It is agreed," the animals said. " That we will do."

The animals sat around the council fire and said, "Who is going to set the sun free?"

"I shall not do it," Deer said. "Whoever sets the sun free must get so close to the sun that he will be burned to death."

"I shall not do it," Lynx said. "Whoever sets the sun free must chew the leather thong that holds the sun. The sun will burn him to death before he can do it."

"I shall not do it," Wildcat said.

"I shall not do it," Possum said.

"I shall not do it," Raccoon said.

"I shall do it," Beaver said.

The animals looked at Beaver. "You will set the sun free? How can you set the sun free? Your teeth are small. They are not even sharp. You can chew only a blade of grass with your teeth. How can you chew the leather thong that holds the sun?"

The animals looked at Beaver. None of the animals liked Beaver. He was small, and his fur was thin. There was not a thing Beaver could do that the other animals could not do better, and when the animals played ball, Beaver was never asked. Beaver sat at the edge of the field and watched the animals play ball. Beaver could not run. He could not carry the ball. None of the animals liked him.

Beaver said again, "I shall set the sun free."

"Let him try," Wildcat said. "He will burn to death, but we will not miss him."

"Let him try," Raccoon said, and the rest of the animals agreed.

"Set the sun free then, if you can," the animals said, and they laughed when they said it.

So Beaver set off toward the place in the sky above the earth where the sun was held by the snare. Beaver was slow. He could not run. He was the slowest of all the animals. Beaver took many days to get to the sun. The sun burned him. It was so bright he had to close his eyes. Beaver did not stop until he came to the place where the sun was.

Beaver began to chew on the leather thong that held the sun. His skin was burning and blistering from the heat. His eyes were dry, hot stones in his head. There was no wetness in his mouth. His tongue was like the leather he was chewing. But he did not stop.

Suddenly he chewed through the leather. The animals saw the sun rise into the sky. The animals felt the cool winds begin to blow on the earth. Beaver had freed the sun.

Beaver lay in the center of the council ring. There was no fur on his body. His skin was burned and scorched and his flesh was falling off his bones. His teeth were only blackened stumps.

He-Who-Made-the-Animals stood in the center of the council ring. "Beaver," he said, "the animals will not forget what you have done for them. I will see that they do not forget."

And he gave Beaver new teeth, broad and flat and so strong that Beaver could cut down the largest trees with them. He gave Beaver a fine fur that was like down on his skin. He gave Beaver a second coat of fur to guard the fine fur underneath. There is no animal with fur so fine.

Cree Indian Tale
Natalia M. Belting

# Snow-White and Rose-Red *

## Characters

| | |
|---|---|
| SNOW-WHITE | BEAR |
| ROSE-RED | DWARF |
| MOTHER | STORYTELLER |

## Act I

(SNOW-WHITE, ROSE-RED, *and their* MOTHER *are sitting before the fire in their cottage in the woods on a winter night.*)

STORYTELLER: There was once a poor woman who lived in a lonely cottage. In front of the cottage was a garden where stood two rose trees, one of which bore white and the other red roses. She had two children who were like the two rose trees, and one was called Snow-White and the other Rose-Red. They were as good and happy, as busy and cheerful, as ever two children could be.

In the winter Snow-White lit the fire and hung the kettle on to boil. And here they are.

MOTHER: Go, Snow-White, and bolt the door. Night is coming and it will soon be time for bed. But first let us have a story.

(SNOW-WHITE *looks out, then bolts the door.*)

SNOW-WHITE: The snow is falling thick and fast. This is no night to be out.

(ROSE-RED *brings a book.*)

MOTHER: What story will it be tonight?

ROSE-RED: Oh, do let us have "The Princess on the Glass Hill."

MOTHER: That's one we all like.

(MOTHER *opens the book and begins to read. A knock is heard at the door.*)

MOTHER: Quick, Rose-Red, open the door. It must be a traveler who is seeking shelter.

(ROSE-RED *pushes back the bolt and opens the door. A* BEAR *puts his head in the door.* ROSE-RED *screams and springs back.* SNOW-WHITE *hides behind* MOTHER.)

281

BEAR: Do not be afraid. I will do you no harm! I am half-frozen, and only want to warm myself a little.

MOTHER: Poor bear, lie down by the fire, only take care that you do not burn your coat. Snow-White, Rose-Red, the bear will do you no harm. He means well.

(SNOW-WHITE *and* ROSE-RED, *still frightened, come forward and stand looking at the* BEAR.)

BEAR: Here, children, knock the snow out of my coat a little.

(*The girls bring a broom and sweep the bear's hide clean. He stretches himself by the fire and growls happily.*)

282

(**SNOW-WHITE** *and* **ROSE-RED** *soon lose their fear of the* **BEAR**, *and begin patting him. Then they pull his hair and roll him about, even hit him with a little switch.*)

**STORYTELLER:** As soon as day dawned, the two children let the bear out, and he trotted across the snow into the forest.

After that the bear came every evening at the same time, laid himself down by the fire, and let the children frolic with him as much as they liked. They got so used to him that the doors were never bolted until their friend had arrived. And then spring came to the forest.

**BEAR:** Now I must go away, and cannot come back for the whole summer.

**283**

**SNOW-WHITE:** Where are you going, dear bear?

**BEAR:** I must go into the forest to guard my treasures from wicked dwarfs. In the winter, when the earth is frozen hard, they have to stay below and cannot work their way through. But now, when the sun has warmed the earth, they break through it, and come out to steal. What once gets into their hands, and into their caves, does not easily see daylight again.

**STORYTELLER:** The girls were sorry to see him go, and as they opened the door for him, and as the bear was hurrying out, he caught against the bolt and a piece of his hairy coat was torn off. It seemed to Snow-White as if she had seen gold shining through it, but she was not sure. The bear ran away quickly and was soon out of sight.

 **Act II**

(SNOW-WHITE *and* ROSE-RED *are walking alongside a brook in the woods. They see a* DWARF *jumping about near the water.*)

ROSE-RED: Where are you going? You surely don't want to go into the water?

DWARF: I am not such a fool! Don't you see that this terrible fish wants to pull me in?

(*The girls try to free his beard from the fishing line in which it is caught, but cannot.*)

SNOW-WHITE: Wait a minute and I will help.

(*She pulls her scissors from her pocket and snips off a bit of his beard.*)

DWARF: Clumsy people, to cut off a piece of my fine beard. Bad luck to you!

(*He runs to the roots of a tree, picks up a bag filled with gold, and goes off.*)

285

# Act III

(**SNOW-WHITE** *and* **ROSE-RED** *are on their way to town to shop. Huge rocks lie on the ground where they are walking.*)

**ROSE-RED** (*looking up*): Look, Snow-White! What is that huge bird flying round and round above us?

**SNOW-WHITE**: I do believe it's an eagle. And see, it flies lower and lower as if it were looking for something. Why, it is lighting on that rock!

(*They hear a loud cry, run to the rock, and see that the eagle has caught the* **DWARF** *and is trying to carry him off. They pull at the little man until the eagle lets him go.*)

**DWARF:** Could you not have done it more carefully? You dragged at my coat so that it is all torn, you clumsy creatures!

(*He picks up a bag of precious stones and runs away. Thinking no one is watching him, he empties the stones on the ground and counts them. The girls tiptoe over to watch.*)

DWARF: Why do you stand there staring? You are always getting in my way!

(*A loud growl is heard, and the* BEAR *approaches. The* DWARF *springs up in fear.*)

288

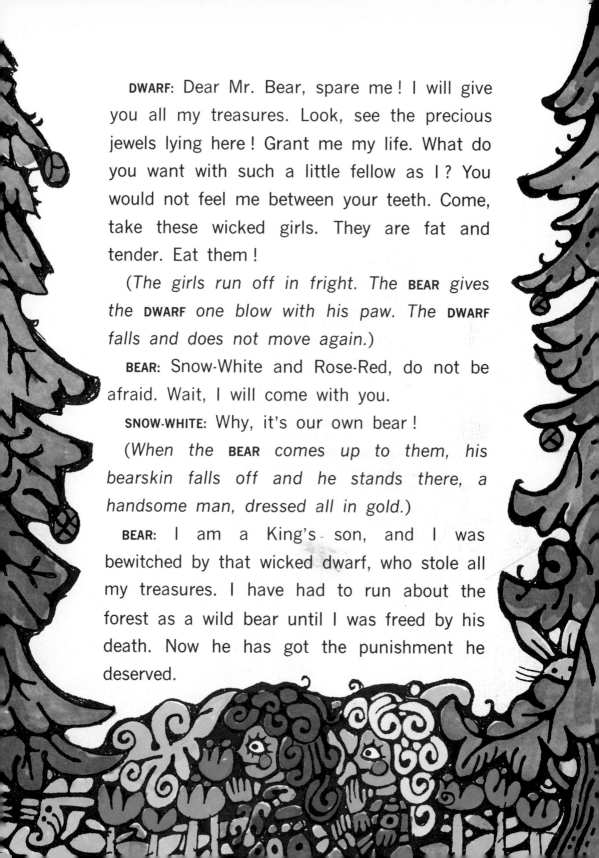

DWARF: Dear Mr. Bear, spare me! I will give you all my treasures. Look, see the precious jewels lying here! Grant me my life. What do you want with such a little fellow as I? You would not feel me between your teeth. Come, take these wicked girls. They are fat and tender. Eat them!

(*The girls run off in fright. The* BEAR *gives the* DWARF *one blow with his paw. The* DWARF *falls and does not move again.*)

BEAR: Snow-White and Rose-Red, do not be afraid. Wait, I will come with you.

SNOW-WHITE: Why, it's our own bear!

(*When the* BEAR *comes up to them, his bearskin falls off and he stands there, a handsome man, dressed all in gold.*)

BEAR: I am a King's son, and I was bewitched by that wicked dwarf, who stole all my treasures. I have had to run about the forest as a wild bear until I was freed by his death. Now he has got the punishment he deserved.

**STORYTELLER:** Snow-White was married to the prince and Rose-Red to his brother, and they divided between them the great treasure which the dwarf had hidden in his cave. Their mother lived happily with her children for many years. She took the two rose trees with her, and they stood before her window, and every year bore the most beautiful roses, white and red.

*German Folk Tale*
*Jacob* and *Wilhelm Grimm*

290

# Adventures of ISABEL

Isabel met an enormous bear,
Isabel, Isabel, didn't care;
The bear was hungry, the bear was ravenous,
The bear's big mouth was cruel and cavernous.
The bear said, Isabel, glad to meet you,
How do, Isabel, now I'll eat you!
Isabel, Isabel, didn't worry,
Isabel didn't scream or scurry.
She washed her hands and she straightened her hair up,
Then Isabel quietly ate the bear up.

*Ogden Nash*

# THE HOLES OF LAGOS

"Lagos!* Where is Lagos?"

"As far as far can be in Mexico."

"What part of Mexico?"

"I can't tell. Maybe any part of Mexico. Some people say one place; some say another; but, wherever that town is, it is full of foolish people."

"Aren't there foolish people everywhere?"

"Everywhere there are *some* fools, but in Lagos they are *all* fools."

"That can't be."

"Oh, yes it can! In Lagos they do things people would do nowhere else. There was the time they found a deep hole in the center of the plaza, not far from the church."

"What happened?"

"Well, this is what happened."

* Lä'gōs

**292**

One morning the mayor of the town was walking in his bare feet across the plaza, on his way to the city hall. When he got near the church, he found a deep hole, big enough for three men to fall into. He stopped and looked at the hole for a long time.

"How did this hole come to be in the plaza of Lagos?" he cried. "Who put it there?"

When no one answered, he called to the policeman, who had a big torn sombrero on his head and a thin stick in his hand.

"How did that hole get there?" cried the mayor.

"I don't know, Señor Alcalde."*

"If you, the keeper of peace in Lagos, do not know, then nobody knows."

"That is true, Señor Alcalde."

"It's dangerous to have a hole like that in our town plaza. People walking to church or to the city hall might fall into it and get hurt."

"Quite true, Señor Alcalde."

"Well, then it must be closed at once."

"That's right, Señor Alcalde."

"Get the men of Lagos at once and have them fill up that hole."

"Si, Señor Alcalde."

The mayor went into the city hall and the policeman went to assemble all the men of Lagos, who were sitting on their heels. They began digging up the earth from a place nearby and threw it into the hole. When the sun sank behind the hill, the hole was filled and the earth over it was smooth as a leaf. Everyone was satisfied with the day's work and went home to eat tortillas.

*Sen nyôr' Äl käl'dā

**294**

Later when the mayor came out of the city hall, the policeman said politely:

"Señor Alcalde, you see that the hole is filled. The men did a fine job."

"I'm glad to hear it. We have good men in our town, better than any in Mexico."

"Thank you, Señor Alcalde."

The mayor walked away. He hadn't walked far until he came to a second hole, the one from which the earth had been taken to fill the first hole. He stopped and looked at it in surprise.

"Another hole!" he exclaimed. "How did this hole get here? Carlos! Carlos!"

The policeman came running.

"Yes, Señor Alcalde."

"There is a hole here. Look!"

"Yes, Señor Alcalde, there is," said Carlos, looking at it.

"People going to church or to the city hall could fall into it and break a leg."

"Well, they might, Señor Alcalde, they really might."

"It must be closed at once, Carlos."

"Yes, it must be closed at once, Señor Alcalde," agreed Carlos, taking off his sombrero and scratching his head, "but the men have all gone home to eat their tortillas and go to bed. Everybody will be sleeping."

"True," said the mayor. "Then tomorrow."

"Tomorrow it will be done, Señor Alcalde."

Early next morning Carlos had the men of Lagos digging up the earth not far from the new hole.

The mayor passed by on the way to his office, watched the men at work, and smiled.

"There are no workmen in all Mexico better than the workmen of Lagos," he said aloud, and went to the city hall.

The men all heard what he said and were pleased, and they worked with greater zeal. Soon the second hole was filled and the earth smoothed down.

At the setting of the sun, the mayor came by and saw the hole filled and the ground over it as smooth as a church floor.

"Carlos, that is good work."

"The men of Lagos are good workers, Señor Alcalde," agreed Carlos.

The mayor walked on; but he hadn't walked far when he came to a new hole.

"Another hole ! Holes grow in Lagos like weeds in a corn patch. How did this hole come to be here ? Carlos ! Carlos !"

Carlos came running.

"What's happened, Señor Alcalde?"

"There's another hole here in the ground. Look, Carlos!"

Carlos looked. "Yes, Señor Alcalde, there is another hole in the ground."

"It is dangerous. It must be filled."

"Yes, it must be filled, Señor Alcalde."

"People crossing the plaza might fall into it and break a leg."

"They might indeed break a leg, Señor."

"Fill it at once."

"The men have all gone home to eat their tortillas, and soon they'll be asleep."

"True," said the mayor, ". . . quite true. Well, then, tomorrow."

"Yes, Señor Alcalde."

This went on and on. Everyone in Lagos tried to figure out how it happened and why there were so many holes in their town, but they couldn't. They were just that kind of people. So they kept on filling holes by digging new holes until they came to the edge of town.

Now, the people of the next town had been watching the work of Lagos day by day, laughing and saying nothing. But when the hole was next to their own town, they filled it with things lying around that they had been wanting to get rid of for a long time.

When the mayor of Lagos saw the last hole filled, and could not find another, he was very happy and said, "The men of Lagos never give up a job until it is finished."

The men of Lagos were happy, too, for they said they were getting a little tired of so much digging every day.

So everyone was happy, and there were no more holes in Lagos.

*Mexican Folk Tale — M. A. Jagendorf*
*and R. S. Boggs*

300

# How Would You Say It ?

People find many different meanings in the sayings below. Choose three of these sayings and tell what you think they mean.

1. He who hesitates is lost.

2. Haste makes waste.

3. Don't count your chickens before they're hatched.

4. A bird in the hand is worth two in the bush.

5. You can't judge a book by its cover.

6. Don't cross your bridges until you come to them.

7. Too many cooks spoil the broth.

8. Many hands make light work.

9. Look before you leap.

10. Once bitten, twice shy.

Write your own fable using one of the sayings above. Or you might like to invent your own saying and write a fable about it.

# All About You

Put your answers on another paper.

1. Think of a word that describes you. Write it. Now write a word that rhymes with the word you have chosen.
2. Write five other names that begin with that same letter as your first name.
3. If A = 1, B = 2, C = 3 and so forth, how much does your first name add up to? your last name?
4. What color are your eyes? Can you list ten things that are the same color as your eyes?
5. List three things you like and tell why.
6. Finish the last two lines of this poem by telling something special about yourself.

> Roses are red,
> Violets are blue,
>
> _____
>
> _____

Look back at all your answers. Now write a paragraph about yourself using as many of the answers which you have already given as you can.

# Jimmy Takes Vanishing Lessons

by Walter R. Brooks

The school bus picked up Jimmy every morning at his aunt's house, and every afternoon it dropped him there again. And so, twice a day, on the bus, he passed that strange, dark, side road through the woods.

The bus driver once pointed it out. "Folks that go in there after dark," he said, "well, they don't ever come out again. There's a haunted house about a quarter of a mile down that road." He paused. "But you ought to know about that, Jimmy. It was your grandfather's house."

Jimmy knew about it, and he knew that it now belonged to his Aunt Mary. But Jimmy's aunt would never talk to him about the house. She said the stories about it were silly, and there were no such things as ghosts.

Jimmy still wondered about the people who had tried to live there. Aunt Mary had rented the house three times, but every family had moved out within a week. They said the things that went on there were just too queer. So, nobody would live in it any more.

"If only I could prove that there isn't a ghost," Jimmy thought.

One day, when his aunt was in the village, Jimmy took the key to the haunted house and started out. "Ghosts aren't around in the daytime," he told himself. But, when he came out in the clearing and looked at those blank, dusty windows, he wasn't so sure.

"Oh, come on!" he told himself. And he waded through the long grass to the porch.

Then he stopped again. His feet did not seem to want to go up the steps. But at last they marched up to the front door, and Jimmy set his teeth hard and put the key in the keyhole. It turned with a squeak. He pushed the door open and went in.

He was in a long, dark hall with closed doors on both sides, and on the right, the stairs went up. He had left the door open behind him, and then, as he stood there, the hall grew darker and darker. The door, all of itself, began to swing shut. And before he could stop it, it closed with a bang. And it was then, as he was pulling at the handle to get out, that Jimmy saw the ghost.

It was a tall, dim, white figure, and it came gliding slowly down the stairs towards him. Jimmy gave a yell, yanked the door open, and tore down the steps. He didn't stop until he was well down the road.

Then he had to get his breath. "Boy!" he said. "I've seen a ghost! Was that awful!" Then after a minute, he thought, "What was so awful about it? He was trying to scare me. Pretty silly business for a grown-up ghost to be doing."

As soon as Jimmy got over his fright, he began to get angry. And he got up and started back. "I must get that key, anyway," he thought, for he had left it in the door.

This time he walked very quietly. He thought he'd just lock the door and go home. But he saw it was still open, and as he reached for the key, he heard a faint sound. He peeked inside and there was the ghost.

The ghost was going back upstairs, but he wasn't gliding now, he was doing a sort of dance, and every other step he would bend double and shake with laughter. He was enjoying the joke he had played. That made Jimmy madder than ever. He stuck his head farther inside the door and yelled, "Boo!" The ghost gave a scream and leaped two feet in the air, then sank on the stairs.

As soon as Jimmy saw that he could scare the ghost even worse than the ghost could scare him, he wasn't afraid any more, and he came right into the hall.

"Oh, my goodness!" gasped the ghost. "You can't *do* that to me!"

"I did it, didn't I?" said Jimmy. "Now we're even."

"Nothing of the kind," said the ghost crossly. "You seem pretty stupid, even for a boy. Ghosts are supposed to scare people. People aren't supposed to scare ghosts. But look here, boy, this could be bad for me if people got to know about it."

"You mean you don't want me to tell anybody about it?" Jimmy asked.

"You keep still about this," the ghost said, "and in return I'll—well, let's see. How would you like to know how to vanish?"

"Oh, that would be swell!" Jimmy said. "But—can you vanish?"

"Sure," said the ghost, and he did. All at once, he wasn't there. Jimmy was alone in the hall. But the voice went right on talking.

"I wish you'd please reappear," Jimmy said. "It makes me feel funny to talk to somebody who isn't there."

"Sorry, I forgot," said the ghost, and there he was again, sitting on the bottom step. Jimmy could see the step, dimly, right through him.

"There's only one thing you can do," said Jimmy, "if I promise not to tell about scaring you. Go live somewhere else. There's Miller's up the road. Nobody lives there any more."

"That old shack!" said the ghost. "Doors and windows half off, roof leaky—no thanks! What do you think it's like in a storm, windows banging, rain dripping on you—I guess not! Peace and quiet, that's what a ghost wants."

"Well, I don't think it's fair," Jimmy said, "for you to live in a house that doesn't belong to you, and keep my aunt from renting it."

"Pooh!" said the ghost. "I'm not stopping her from renting it. I don't take up any room, and it's not my fault if people get scared and leave."

"Yes it is!" Jimmy said. "You don't play fair. I'm telling everybody how I scared you."

"Oh, you mustn't do that! If that got out, every ghost in the country would really be in terrible trouble."

At last Jimmy said, "Well, all right. You teach me to vanish and I won't tell."

Jimmy didn't say anything to his aunt about what he'd done. But every Saturday, he went to the haunted house for his vanishing lesson. It is really quite easy when you know how. In a couple of weeks he could flicker, and in six weeks the ghost said he was very good for a boy. So, he thanked the ghost and shook hands with him and said, "Well, good-by now. You'll hear from me."

That night at supper, Jimmy's aunt said, "Well, what have you been doing today?"

"I've been learning to vanish."

His aunt smiled. "That must be fun."

"The ghost up at Grandfather's taught me," said Jimmy.

"I don't think that's very funny," said his aunt. "And will you please not—why, where are you?" she cried, for he had vanished.

"Here," he said as he reappeared.

"Oh, my goodness!" she cried, and she pushed back her chair and rubbed her eyes.

Jimmy had to vanish twice more before she would believe it. She was pretty upset. When she was more quiet, they had a long talk. Jimmy kept his word and didn't tell her about scaring the ghost. But he said he had a plan, and at last she promised to help.

So, the next day, she went to the old house and started to work. She opened the windows and swept and dusted, and made as much noise as possible.

Soon the ghost came floating into the room where she was sweeping. She was scared all right. She gave a yell and threw the broom at him. The broom went right through him and he came nearer, waving his arms and groaning.

Jimmy suddenly appeared and jumped at the ghost with a "Boo!" And the ghost fell over in a dead faint.

As soon as Jimmy's aunt saw that, she wasn't frightened any more. She found some smelling salts and held them under the ghost's nose. At last he sat up and said to Jimmy, "You broke your word!"

"I promised not to *tell* about scaring you, but I didn't promise not to scare you."

His aunt said, "You really are a ghost, aren't you? I thought you were just stories people made up. Well, I must get on with my work." And she began sweeping and banging around with her broom harder than ever.

The ghost put his hands to his head. "All this noise," he said. "Couldn't you work more quietly, ma'am?"

"Whose house is this, anyway?" she demanded. "If you don't like it, why don't you move out?"

The ghost sneezed fiercely several times. "Excuse me," he said. "You're raising so much dust. Where's that boy?" he asked suddenly. For Jimmy had vanished again.

"I'm sure I don't know," she replied. "Probably getting ready to scare you again."

"You ought to have better control of him," said the ghost severely. "If he was my boy, I'd take a hairbrush to him."

"You have my permission," she said, and she reached right through the ghost and pulled the chair cushion out from under him and began banging the dust out of it. "What's more," she went on, as he got up and glided wearily to another chair, "Jimmy and I are going to sleep here nights from now on, and I don't think it would be very smart of you to try any tricks."

"Ha, ha," said the ghost nastily. "He who laughs last—"

"Ha, ha, yourself," said Jimmy's voice from close behind him. "And that's me, laughing last."

The ghost muttered and vanished.

Jimmy's aunt put cotton in her ears and slept that night in the best bedroom with the light lit. The ghost screamed for awhile down in the cellar, but nothing happened, so he came upstairs. He thought that he would appear to her as two glaring, flaming eyes, which was one of his best tricks, but first he wanted to be sure where Jimmy was. But he couldn't find him.

He hunted all over the house, and though he was invisible himself, he got more and more nervous. He kept imagining that, at any moment, Jimmy might jump out at him from some dark corner and scare him into fits. Finally, he got so jittery that he went back to the cellar and hid all night.

The next days were just as bad for the ghost. Several times he tried to scare Jimmy's aunt while she was working, but she didn't scare worth a cent, and twice Jimmy managed to sneak up on him and appear suddenly with a loud yell, frightening him dreadfully.

He was rather timid even for a ghost. He began to look quite haggard. He had long arguments with Jimmy's aunt, in which he wept and appealed to her kindness, but she was firm. If he wanted to live there, he would have to pay rent, just like anybody else. The abandoned Miller farm was two miles up the road. Why didn't he move there?

When the house was all in apple-pie order, Jimmy's aunt went to see a Mr. and Mrs. Whistler, who were living at the hotel because they couldn't find a house to move into. She told them about the old house, but they said, "No, thank you. We've heard about that house. It's haunted. *You* wouldn't dare spend a night there."

She told him that she and Jimmy had spent the last week there, but they didn't believe her. So she said, "If you want to rent it, I will let Jimmy stay there with you until you are sure everything is all right."

At last they said that they would rent it. So they moved in. Jimmy stayed there for a week, but he saw nothing of the ghost. And then one of the boys at school told him that somebody had seen a ghost up at the Miller farm. So Jimmy knew the ghost had taken his aunt's advice.

A day or two later, he walked up to the Miller farm. There was no front door and he walked right in. There was some groaning and thumping upstairs, and then the ghost came floating down.

"Oh, it's you!" he said. "Goodness, boy, can't you leave me in peace?"

Jimmy said he'd just come up to see how the ghost was getting along.

"Getting along fine," said the ghost. "Peaceful. Quiet. Nobody playing silly tricks."

"Well," said Jimmy. "I won't bother you if you won't bother the Whistlers. But if you come back there—"

"Don't worry," said the ghost.

So, with the rent money, Jimmy and his aunt had a much easier life. They went to the movies, and Jimmy had new clothes, and on Thanksgiving they had a turkey. The ghost even came down to Thanksgiving dinner, though he couldn't eat much. He seemed to enjoy the warmth of the house and he taught Jimmy several more tricks.

He was really a pretty good fellow, as ghosts go, and Jimmy's aunt got quite fond of him herself. When the real winter weather began, she worried about him because there was no heat in the Miller place and there was hardly any roof. The ghost tried to tell her that heat and cold didn't bother ghosts at all.

"Maybe not," she said, "but just the same, it can't be very pleasant." And when he said he would come for Christmas dinner, she made him some warm slippers, and he was so pleased that he broke down and cried. And that made Jimmy's aunt so happy, *she* broke down and cried.

Jimmy didn't cry, but he said, "Aunt Mary, don't you think it would be nice if the ghost came to live with us this winter?"

"I would feel very much better about him if he did," she said.

So, the ghost stayed with them that winter, and then he just stayed on, and it must have been a peaceful place for, the last I heard, he was still there.

# Glossary

The list below is called a pronunciation key. The pronunciation key gives symbols and key words for the vowel sounds and the consonant sounds. This key will help you to pronounce the words in the glossary.

| | | | | | | | |
|---|---|---|---|---|---|---|---|
| a | hat | i | it | p | pen | v | very |
| ā | face | ī | five | r | run | w | will |
| ã | care | | | s | say | y | yes |
| ä | father | j | jam | sh | she | z | zoo |
| | | k | kind | t | tell | zh | measure |
| b | bad | l | land | th | thin | | |
| ch | child | m | me | ŦH | then | | |
| d | did | n | no | | | ə | represents: |
| | | ng | bring | u | cup | | a in about |
| e | let | | | ů | put | | e in children |
| ē | be | o | hot | ü | rude | | i in magnify |
| ėr | her | ō | go | ū | use | | o in parrot |
| | | ô | or | | | | u in circus |
| f | fat | oi | voice | | | | |
| g | go | ou | out | | | | |
| h | he | | | | | | |

The pronunciation system and key are from *Thorndike Barnhart Beginning Dictionary*. Copyright © 1968 by Scott, Foresman and Company.

**abandon**

## A

**aban don** (ə ban′dən). 1. to forsake or desert; to leave without meaning to return: *to abandon an old house.* 2. to give up completely.

**aban doned** (ə ban′dənd). forsaken; deserted: *an abandoned village.*

**ad mi ra tion** (ad′mə rā′shən). 1. a feeling of pleasure and approval, mixed with wonder, at something fine, great, beautiful, or well done. 2. someone or something that causes a feeling of wonder and pleasure.

**ancestor**

**ad mire** (ad mīr′). to look at or think about with wonder, pleasure, and approval: *to admire a brave person.*

**ad vice** (ad vīs′). a recommendation or an opinion about what to do.

**al tar** (ôl′tər). 1. a table or stand in a church at which acts of worship are performed by clergymen. 2. a raised place of earth or stone on which offerings are made to a god or gods.

**al ter** (ôl′tər). to change partly; to make different in some way.

**an ces tor** (an′ses tər). a person from whom another is descended.

**an cient** (ān′shənt). 1. of or having to do with times that are long past: *ancient customs.* 2. a person who lived at a time that is long past.

**ap peal** (ə pēl′). 1. to make an earnest request; to ask in a sincere and serious way, as for help or sympathy. 2. an earnest request.

**ap pre ci ate** (ə prē′shē āt). 1. to see the worth of; to think highly of; to value. 2. to be grateful or thankful for: *to appreciate a kindness.*

**ap proach** (ə prōch′). 1. to come near or draw close: *to approach a building.* 2. the act of coming near or drawing close.

**arch** (ärch). 1. a curved or rounded part of a structure, as of a doorway, window, or bridge. 2. a monument in the form of an arch. 3. the part of the foot between the toes and ankle; the instep. 4. to form an arch over; to span.

**ar gu ment** (är′gū mənt). 1. a discussion by persons who do not agree; a dispute. 2. a reason offered for or against something.

**as sem ble** (ə sem′bl). 1. to bring together or to come together in one place; to meet. 2. to fit or put together the parts of: *to assemble a model ship.*

**astir** (ə stėr′). moving about; in motion; also, out of bed; up.

**as tron o my** (əs tron′ə mē). the science of the sun, planets, moon, stars, and other heavenly bodies.

**a void** (ə void′). to keep out of the way of; to keep away from.

## B

**bam boo** (bam bü′). a treelike grass that grows in warm regions. The strong, hollow stems of some kinds of bamboo are used for canes, fishing poles, furniture, and sometimes for houses.

**bar racks** (bar′əks). 1. a building or set of buildings for soldiers to live in, especially when on duty at a fort. 2. a building in which the state police have offices and in which there are usually rooms for some of the officers to live in.

**bat ter** (bat′ər). a thin mixture made up of flour, milk, eggs used to make such foods as biscuits and cakes.

**bat ter** (bat′ər). in some games, such as baseball and cricket, the player whose turn it is to bat.

**bat ter** (bat′ər). to beat with repeated blows, so as to damage, break, or put out of shape.

**bat tered** (bat′ərd). worn down, damaged; put out of shape by hard use.

**bay** (bā). 1. a stand made by a hunted animal obliged to face those hunting it. 2. a long, deep bark like that made by a dog in hunting. 3. to bark with long, deep tones.

**bay** (bā). a part of a sea or other large body of water, such as a lake, that extends into the land.

**be witch** (bi wich′). 1. to put under a spell; to get an influence over a person by magic. 2. to please very much; to fascinate; to charm.

**bleak** (blēk). 1. cheerless; dreary; dismal. 2. swept by winds; exposed to wind or weather: *a bleak land.* 3. cold and cutting: *to face a bleak wind.*

**bon net** (bon′it). 1. a head covering, usually tied under the chin with ribbon or strings. 2. a soft woolen cap worn by men and boys in Scotland.

**brace and bit** (brās,  bit). a tool for boring holes, consisting of a drill (the bit) fitted into a handle (the brace).

**break er** (brāk′ər). a wave that breaks into foam on the shore or against rocks.

**breed** (brēd). 1. a kind of animal; a race or stock. 2. to give birth to; to produce young. 3. to raise, as cows or horses.

**bulge** (bulj). 1. to swell or puff outward. 2. an outward swelling; a part with an outward bend.

**bulk i er** (bul′kē ər). *From* **bulky.** more bulky; taking up more space; also, harder to handle; clumsier.


**C**

**cac tus** (kak′təs). any one of a large group of plants with fleshy stems, usually with spines or prickles but no leaves.

**calm** (käm). 1. quiet; peaceful; not excited: *to speak in a calm way.* 2. not windy or stormy; not rough: *a calm sea.* 3. freedom from motion or disturbance; quietness. 4. to make calm; to quiet: *to calm a crying child.*

**ca nal** (kə nal′). an artificial waterway; a waterway that has been dug across land for the use of ships or for carrying water to dry land.

**cap i tal** (kap′ə tl). the city where a country or state government is located: *the capital of the United States.*

**Cap i tol** (kap′ə tl). 1. the building in Washington D.C. where the United States Congress meets. 2. a building in which a state legislative body meets.

**cel e bra tion** (sel′ə brā′shən). 1. the activities or special services in honor of somebody or something. 2. the act of celebrating.

**chant er** (chan′tər). 1. in a bagpipe, the pipe on which the melody or tune is played. 2. one who chants; a singer.

**char coal** (chär′kol′). a black or very dark substance made by partly burning wood or other substances in a special oven and used as a fuel, in filters, and in drawing.

**chop sticks** (chop′stiks′). small sticks of wood, ivory, or the like, used in pairs to carry food to the mouth.

**clap** (klap). 1. to strike or slap with the open hand. 2. to strike the open hands together in applause. 3. a loud, noisy crash, such as a sudden burst of thunder. 4. a hard slap.

**clum sy** (klum′zē). 1. not graceful in moving; awkward. 2. poorly made or shaped: *a clumsy chair.*

**clutch** (kluch). 1. a tight grasp or grip. 2. a device in a machine used to connect or disconnect the motor or engine that makes it run. 3. to grasp or grip tightly.

**328**

**col o ny** (kol′ ə nē). 1. a group of persons who move from their own country to settle in another land, but who remain citizens of their own country. 2. a settlement made by such a group of persons.

**com mand ing of fi cer** (kə mand′ing ôf′ə sər). a commander; an officer who is in charge of an army unit or units, a camp, warship, aircraft, or the like.

**conch** (kongk). a large sea shell with a spiral, or coiled, shape.

**con trap tion** (kən trap′shən). a contrivance; a gadget; a mechanical device; an invention.

**coun cil** (koun′sl). 1. a number of persons meeting together to discuss and give advice or to settle questions. 2. a small number of persons elected or appointed to manage and make laws for a city or town.

**coun se lor** (koun′sə lər). 1. a person who gives advice; an adviser. 2. a person whose work is to give advice, especially in legal matters; a lawyer.

**court** (kôrt). 1. a place where trials are held and justice is administered. 2. an open space partly or wholly surrounded by buildings. 3. a space marked off for a game: *a tennis court.* 4. the household or followers of a king or other ruler. 5. to try to gain the affection of; to seek to marry.

**cred it** (kred′it). 1. trust in a person's ability and intention to pay at a later time for something bought. 2. one's reputation in matters of money: *good credit.* 3. a source of honor: *a credit to his country.*

**crin kle** (kring′kl). 1. to make little creases in; to wrinkle. 2. to make soft sounds; to rustle, as silk does.

**crit ter** (krit′ər). *in common speech.* a creature; any person or animal.

## D

**de cay** (di kā′). 1. to change slowly from a good condition to a bad one; to spoil; to rot.

**ded i cate** (ded′ə kāt). 1. to set apart for a special purpose: *to dedicate a church.* 2. to inscribe a book or other work to someone as a sign of respect, gratitude, or affection.

**des per ate ly** (des′pər it lē). in a desperate way; recklessly; frantically.

**de spite** (di spīt′). in spite of.

**dry-wash** (drī′wosh′). 1. in western United States, a rocky stream-bed, usually dry but at times filled with rushing water. 2. clothes washed and dried but not ironed.

## E

**e di tion** (i dish′ən). 1. all the copies of a book, magazine, or newspaper printed alike at the same time. 2. the form in which a book is published: *a new illustrated edition.*

hat, fāce, cāre, fäther, let, bē, hèr, it, fīve, hot, gō, ôr, voice, out, thin, ŦHen, cup, ūse, pùt, rüde. ə stands for *a* in about, *e* in children, *i* in magnify, *o* in parrot, and *u* in circus.

**el e gant** (el′ə gənt). having or showing very good taste; also, marked by gracefulness and beauty.

**en dur ance** (en dur′əns or en dyur′ans). ability to endure or last; power to continue under hardship without being overcome or destroyed.

**en gi neer** (en′jə nir′). 1. one who takes care of, builds, or runs engines. 2. one who designs and builds machines, bridges, roads, forts, canals, and the like. 3. to manage or guide.

**enor mous** (i nôr′məs). very large; huge.

**ex pen sive** (eks pen′siv). of a high price; costly.

**ex pert** (eks′pért). 1. a person who has special skill, knowledge about a particular thing. 2. (eks pért′). having or showing special knowledge; skillful; clever: *an expert skater.*

### F

**fan cy** (fan′sē). 1. to picture to oneself; to imagine. 2. to be fond of; to like: *to fancy bright colors.* 3. imagination. 4. a liking, as of someone or something. 5. not ordinary; ornamental.

**fa vor** (fā′vər). 1. a kind act: *to do a favor for a neighbor.* 2. strong liking; approval: *to look with favor on a plan for a picnic.* 3. to think well of; to like. 4. in favor of; on the side of.

**fer ry** (fer′ē). 1. a boat that carries people and goods back and forth across a body of water, such as a river or bay. 2. to carry people and goods across a stretch of water in a boat. 3. to cross a stretch of water on a ferry.

**flute** (flüt). a musical instrument in the form of a slender hollow tube open only at one end.

**foun tain** (fount′ n). 1. a jet or stream of water rising in the air in a spray; also, the pipes that carry the water and the basin into which it flows. 2. a place where one can get a drink.

### G

**glare** (glār). 1. a strong, dazzling light; a bright, unpleasant light. 2. a fierce, angry look. 3. to shine with a bright light. 4. to stare in an angry way.

**guard i an** (gär′dē ən). 1. a person who guards or takes care of some other person or some special thing. 2. a person appointed by law to take care of another person or of his property.

### H

**hag gard** (hag′ərd). looking worn, as from weariness, worry, or pain.

**har vest** (här′vist). 1. to reap and gather in grain; to gather in any food crop. 2. the gathering in of crops. 3. the season or time of the harvest.

**hast y** (hās′tē). 1. quick; hurried; *a hasty look.* 2. done or decided without careful thought: a hasty answer. 3. having a quick temper.

**hatch** (hach). 1. an opening in the deck of a ship. 2. an opening or door in an aircraft. 3. an opening in the floor or roof of a building; also, the covering of such an opening.

**hatch** (hach). 1. to bring forth young from eggs, as does a hen. 2. to come forth from an egg as does a chicken. 3. to think up; to plot: *to hatch a plan.*

**ha zel** (hā′zl). 1. light brown color. 2. a bush or small tree that bears light brown nuts that are good to eat.

**hearth** (härth). 1. the floor of a fireplace. 2. the fireside; the home itself.

**hill ock** (hil′ək). a small hill.

**hoist** (hoist). 1. to lift up; to raise, especially with ropes or pulleys. 2. an apparatus used to lift or raise. 3. a lift; a boost.

**hu man** (hū′mən). 1. of or having to do with people: *the human race.* 2. having the form or special qualities of people: *a human being.*

**hur ri cane** (hėr′ə kān). a violent windstorm, usually with heavy rain, which occurs mainly in tropical regions.

**I**

**in de pend ence** (in′di pen′dəns). condition of being independent: freedom from the control, influence, or help of another or others.

**in ex pen sive** (in′eks pen′siv). not expensive; not high in price; cheap.

**in tel li gent** (in tel′ə jənt). having intelligence; able to learn and understand.

**in vis i ble** (in viz′ ə bl). not visible, not able to be seen.

**J**

**josh** (josh). to make fun of in a good-natured way; to tease in a playful way.

**K**

**keen** (kēn). 1. having a fine edge; not dull: *a knife with a keen blade.* 2. strong; sharp: *keen eyesight.* 3. stinging: *a keen wind.* 4. having mental sharpness: *a keen mind.*

**ki mo no** (kə mō′nə). 1. a loose outer garment, held in place with a sash, worn by both men and women in Japan. 2. a loose dressing gown somewhat like a kimono worn by women in other countries.

**L**

**lim ber** (lim′bər). 1. bending easily; able to twist and turn easily.

**loy al** (loi′əl). 1. faithful; worthy of trust: *a loyal friend.* 2. faithful to one's government: *a loyal citizen.*

**lynx** (lingks). an animal that looks somewhat like a household cat, but is larger; a bobcat or wildcat.

**M**

**mam my lor ry** (mam′ē lôr′ē). a type of truck fitted out to serve as a bus for people, as well as to carry farm products and some kinds of farm animals, such as chickens, and the like.

**man go** (mang′gō). 1. a tree of warm regions that bears a slightly sour, juicy fruit, with a thick yellowish-red rind. 2. the fruit of this tree.

hat, fāce, cāre, fäther, let, bē, hėr, it, fīve, hot, gō, ôr, voice, out, thin, ŦHen, cup, ūse, pùt, rüde. ə stands for a in about, e in children, i in magnify, o in parrot, and u in circus.

**mare** (mãr). a female horse; also, the female of certain other animals, such as the donkey.

**mem o ry** (mem'ə rē). 1. ability to remember or recall what has been learned. 2. all that is remembered by a person.

**mes quite** (mes kēt'). a spiny tree or shrub of southwestern United States and Mexico that bears beanlike pods.

**mold** (mōld). 1. a hollow shape in which something is formed: *a mold for jelly.* 2. to form or make into a certain shape.

**mold** (mōld). 1. a light, furry growth that may appear on food and other vegetable or animal substances kept too long in a warm, damp place. 2. to become covered with mold.

**moor** (mụr). an area of open waste land on which heather grows.

**moor** (mụr). to put or keep in place, as a ship, with ropes, chains, or anchors.

**muf fle** (muf'əl). 1. to wrap or cover up so as to keep warm or protect in some way: *to muffle one's head in a woolen scarf.* 2. to soften or deaden the sound of.

**munch** (munch). to chew steadily; to chew with a crunching sound.

**N**

**no ble** (nō'bl). 1. great in character; of great virtue or goodness: *a noble person.* 2. of high rank or position in life: *of noble birth.* 3. having very fine qualities: *a noble animal.* 4. a person of high rank or birth; a nobleman.

**O**

**ob ser va tion** (ob'zər vā'shən). 1. the act or power of seeing and noting something. 2. something seen and noted. 3. the fact of being seen: *to try to avoid observation.* 4. a remark: *to make an observation.* 5. for use in viewing or looking closely at something: *an observation tower.*

**oco til lo** (ō'kə tēl'yō *or* ō'kə tē'yō). a woody shrub or tree with scarlet flowers which grows in southwestern United States and Mexico.

**ol la** (ol'ə). 1. a water jar or cooking pot made of baked clay. 2. a highly seasoned stew cooked in a clay pot.

**P**

**peck** (pek). 1. a unit of dry measure; eight quarts or a fourth of a bushel. 2. a large quantity; a great deal.

**peck** (pek). 1. to pick up food with the beak, as a hen does. 2. to strike, as with the beak.

**ped es tal** (ped'is tl). 1. the support or base on which a column or statue stands. 2. the base of a tall lamp, vase, or the like.

**perk** (pėrk). 1. to lift up or move one's body or head in a saucy, bold, or brisk way. 2. to become lively.

**pis ton** (pis'tən). a sliding piece, usually a short cylinder or roller-shaped body, that moves back and forth inside a larger cylinder and is moved by steam in a steam engine and by fuel exploding in a car.

**pitch black** (pich′blak′). as black or dark as pitch, a very dark or black, sticky substance.

**pla za** (plä′zə). a public square in a city or town.

**pop u lar** (pop′yə lər). 1. liked by, or pleasing to, many persons: *a popular game.* 2. liked by one's associates: *a popular person.* 3. common; widespread; also, in general use.

**prod uce** (prod′üs or prod′ūs). 1. the yield or product, as of a farm. 2. (prə düs′ or prə dūs′). to bring forth; to yield: *to produce a good crop.* 3. to manufacture; to make.

**proof er** (prüf′ər). in a bakery, the room or box-like compartment where uncooked bread and rolls are put to "proof," or rise, before being baked.

**pro tec tor** (prə tek′tər). 1. someone who protects; a guardian; a defender. 2. something that serves to protect.

### R

**ram** (ram). 1. a male sheep. 2. a machine used to strike heavy blows, as in breaking down a wall. 3. to force or press down or in: *to ram a post into the ground.* 5. to butt or strike against with force.

**ra ma da** (rä mä′thä). *a Spanish-American word.* a kind of arbor; a structure of frames or supports covered with vines or branches for shade.

**ra ven** (rā′vən). a large black bird, much like a crow but larger.

**re ap pear** (rē′ə pir′). to appear again

**re late** (ri lāt′). 1. to connect in meaning or thought; to have or fix a relationship between. 2. to give an account of; to tell: *to relate a story.*

**re main** (ri mān′). to stay or continue in a place: *to remain in one's home town.*

**re mark a ble** (ri mär′kə bl). worthy of being noticed; extraordinary.

**res cue squad** (res′kū skwod). a unit of a fire department made up of a small group of men who respond to all emergency calls, not only to a fire but to do such things as rescue a drowning person, give first aid to an injured person, or take a sick person to a hospital.

**re signed** (ri zīnd′). accepting that which happens without resisting; uncomplaining; submissive.

**rum mage** (rum′ij). 1. to make a careful search by moving things about, often in a disorderly way. 2. a careful search in which things are moved about or looked into: *a rummage through a trunk.*

### S

**sac ri fice** (sak′rə fīs). 1. the act of making an offering to a god or gods. especially on an altar. 2. that which is offered as a religious act. 3. to give or offer as a sacrifice. 4. to give up: *to sacrifice one's own life to save the life of another.*

hat, fāce, cāre, fäther, let, bē, hėr, it, fīve, hot, gō, ôr, voice, out, thin, THen, cup, ūse, pùt, rüde. ə stands for *a* in about, *e* in children, *i* in magnify, *o* in parrot, and *u* in circus.

**333**

**san** (sän). *a Japanese word* added to a person's name as a sign of regard or as a title of respect and sometimes added to the name of an object.

**sass** (sas). *in common speech.* **sauce** (sôs). rudeness; act of being rude or impolite, as in making a statement or answering a question.

**sat is fac tion** (sat′is fak′shən). 1. the condition of being satisfied; a state of pleasure and contentment.

**scale** (skāl). 1. to climb by, or as if by, a series of steps. 2. a series of degrees: *a scale of prices.* 3. a series of spaces marked by lines used in measuring, as on a thermometer. 4. in music, a series of tones that go up or down in pitch. 5. an instrument or machine for weighing.

**scale** (skāl). one of the many small, hard plates on the body of some animals, such as fish and snakes.

**scent** (sent). 1. a smell; an odor: *the scent of flowers.* 2. the sense of smell: *a keen scent.* 3. to follow by means of the sense of smell. 4. to fill with odor: to perfume, as a room. 5. perfume.

**scur ry** (skėr′ē). 1. to run in a quick and hurried way; to scamper.

**serge** (sėrj). a kind of woolen cloth with slanting ridges on its surface.

**se vere ly** (sə vir′li). in a severe way; sternly; harshly.

**shaft** (shaft). 1. the long, slender handle of a weapon, such as a spear. 2. an arrow, spear, or the like. 3. a long, narrow space, somewhat like a well. 4. a deep passage made in the earth: *the shaft of a mine.*

**shim my** (shim′ē). 1. to shake or vibrate in an unusual way. 2. to dance with much shaking of the body. 3. an unusual shaking or vibrating. 4. a dance with much shaking of the body.

**sky scrap er** (skī′skrāp′ər). a very tall building.

**snare** (snãr). 1. a noose used for catching birds and small animals. 2. entangle with a noose.

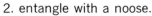

**snow plow** (snō′ plou′). a plow, or device that works like a plow, used to clear away snow.

**som brer o** (som brãr′ō). a broad-brimmed hat, usually of felt, originally worn in Spain, now also worn in Spanish-American countries and southwestern United States.

**spi ral** (spī′rəl). 1. a winding coil that gradually widens. 2. to wind around a central point in circles that gradually grow larger. 3. shaped like a spiral.

**stat ue** (stach′ü). the image or likeness of a person or animal carved or molded in some solid substance, such as wood, marble, bronze, or the like.

**stern** (stėrn). the after part, or rear part, of a ship or boat.

**stern** (stėrn). harsh or severe in manner or nature; strict.

**strand** (strand). 1. to run, drift, or drive upon the shore; to run aground: *to strand a ship.* 2. to come, bring, or place into a helpless position: *to be stranded on a desert island.* 3. a shore; land that borders a body of water, such as a sea or lake.

**strand** (strand). one of the fibers, threads, or strings, that are twisted together into a cord or rope.

**sub way** (sub'wā'). 1. an electric railway that runs beneath the streets of a city. 2. an underground passage.

**suc tion pump** (suk'shən pump). a type of pump that draws a liquid, or other substance, into a space by sucking out or removing part of the air.

**sur vey or** (sər vā'ər). 1. one who examines, views, or looks over to determine a situation, condition, or worth. 2. one who measures boundaries or position: *a land surveyor.*

**sus pect** (səs pekt'). 1. to believe to be guilty without proof. 2. to doubt; to lack faith or confidence in: *to suspect a person's honesty.* 3. to think likely; to guess. 4. (sus'pekt). a person suspected, as of being a thief.

**swerve** (swėrv). 1. to turn to one side; to go out of a straight line or course.

**sym pa thy** (sim'pə thē). 1. a feeling for another person's sorrow or trouble; pity. 2. an inclination or tendency to agree with or support: *to be in sympathy with some person's plan.* 3. an expression of sorrow for another's trouble, loss, or grief.

## T

**tab let** (tab'lit). 1. a flat sheet of some material, such as bronze, bearing an inscription. 2. sheets of paper fastened together, used for writing letters, notes, or the like.

**tea house** (tē'hous'). 1. a type of restaurant found mainly in China and Japan. 2. a place where light meals are served and tea is a specialty

**tel e scope** (tel'ə skōp). an optical instrument used to make distant objects seem larger and nearer.

**tel e type** (tel'ə tīp). 1. a kind of printing telegraph for sending and receiving messages by two instruments that resemble typewriters. 2. to send a message by teletype.

**tem ple** (tem'pl). a building for worship or religious services.

**tem ple** (tem'pl). the flattened part on either side of a person's forehead.

**thatch** (thach). 1. the straw, rushes, or reeds used as a roof or covering on a house or hut. 2. to cover with thatch.

**thong** (thông). 1. a narrow strip of leather, used for fastening something. 2. the lash of a rein, a whip.

**tim id** (tim'id). 1. easily frightened; feeling or showing a lack of courage. 2. shy; bashful: *a timid child.*

**tin gle** (ting'gl). a stinging or prickling feeling, such as might be caused by cold.

**ton** (tun). a measure of weight equal to 2000 pounds in the United States and Canada; 2240 pounds in England.

**tor til la** (tôr tē'yə). *a Spanish-American word.* a thin, flat cake of corn meal baked on a heated stone or iron.

hat, fāce, cãre, fäther, let, bē, hėr, it, fīve, hot, gō, ôr, voice, out, thin, ŦHen, cup, ūse, pùt, rüde. ə stands for *a* in about, *e* in children, *i* in magnify, *o* in parrot, and *u* in circus.

**tor toise shell** (tôr′təs shel).   1. the spotted brown-and-yellow shell of a tortoise.   2. a domestic cat with black-and-yellow spots.   3. a butterfly spotted with yellow and black.   4. made of tortoise shell or having the colors of a tortoise shell.

**tri um phant** (trī um′fənt).  1. joyful because of success or victory.  2. successful; victorious.

**troop er** (trüp′ər).   1. a soldier in a cavalry unit, a military force on horseback.   2. a policeman on horseback.   3. a member of a state police force.

**tuck er** (tuk′ər). *in common speech.* to make very weary or tired; to exhaust.

**tur quoise** (tėr′koiz or tėr′kwoiz).   1. a blue or bluish-green stone valued as a gem.   2. the color of turquoise.

**twi light** (twī′līt′). the faint light that is reflected from the sky just before sunrise or just after sunset.

**twirl** (twėrl).  1. to turn round rapidly; to spin; to whirl.  2. a rapid spinning or whirling motion, as in a dance.

## V

**val ley** (val′ē).  1. a low land between ranges of mountains or hills.  2. an area drained by a river system.

**val ue** (val′ū).  1. worth in money: *the value of a gold watch.*  2. benefit; importance: *the value of proper food.*  3. to estimate the worth of in money: *to value a building.*  4. to appreciate; to regard highly: *to value a friend.*

**vi o lent ly** (vī′ə lənt lē).  in a violent way; with much force.

## W

**wail** (wāl).  1. to cry in a loud and mournful way; to weep, as in grief or pain.  2. a long, loud, mournful cry. *the wail of a baby*

**ward** (wôrd).   1. a division of a hospital.   2. a district of a city or town.   3. a person, especially a child, under the care of a guardian.

**ware house** (wãr′hous′). a building in which goods or other products are kept, generally for future use; a storehouse.

**wea ri ly** (wir′ə le).  in a weary, or tired, way; tiredly.

**wedge** (wej).  1. a piece of wood or metal with a thin edge, used to split or separate something, such as wood or rocks.  2. to split or separate with a wedge.  3. to crowd in tightly; to squeeze in: *to wedge oneself into a crowded bus.*

**wisp y** (wis′pē). like a wisp, or small bunch or strand; slender: a wispy cloud.

**wist ful ly** (wist′fəl eē). in a wistful way; with yearning or longing.

**with er** (wiŦH′ər).   1. to become or make lifeless, sapless, and dry; shrivel; fade.   2. to lose strength, freshness or force.  3. to cause to be ashamed or speechless.

## Z

**zeal** (zēl). much enthusiasm; eager effort.

**336**